PRENTICE HALL
LITERATURE

PENGUIN EDITION

Teaching Resources

Unit 3
A Growing Nation

The American Experience

PEARSON

Prentice Hall

Upper Saddle River, New Jersey
Boston, Massachusetts

ISBN 0-13-165221-4

1 2 3 4 5 6 7 8 9 10   09 08 07 06 05

Contents

UNIT 3

Unit Map 1

Diagnostic Test 3 2

Unit Introduction: Names and Terms to Know 5

Unit Introduction: Focus Questions 6

"The Devil and Tom Walker" by Washington Irving
    Vocabulary and Reading Warm-ups 7
    Literary Analysis: Omniscient Point of View 11
    Reading Strategy: Inferring Cultural Attitudes 12
    Vocabulary Builder 13
    Grammar and Style: Adjective Clauses 14
    Support for Writing Lesson 15
    Support for Extend Your Learning 16
    Enrichment: Narrative Point of View 17
    Selection Test A 18
    Selection Test B 21

"The Tide Rises, The Tide Falls" by Henry Wadsworth Longfellow
"Thanatopsis" by William Cullen Bryant
"Old Ironsides" by Oliver Wendell Holmes
from *Snowbound* by John Greenleaf Whittier
    Vocabulary and Reading Warm-ups 24
    Literary Analysis: Meter 28
    Reading Strategy: Summarizing 29
    Vocabulary Builder 30
    Grammar and Style: Participles as Adjectives 31
    Support for Writing Lesson 32
    Support for Extend Your Learning 33
    Enrichment: Science 34
    Selection Test A 35
    Selection Test B 38

"Crossing the Great Divide" by Meriwether Lewis

"The Most Sublime Spectacle on Earth" by John Wesley Powell

Vocabulary and Reading Warm-ups 41
Literary Analysis: Description 45
Reading Strategy: Noting Spatial Relationships 46
Vocabulary Builder 47
Grammar and Style: Participial Phrases 48
Support for Writing Lesson 49
Support for Extend Your Learning 50
Enrichment: Social Studies 51
Selection Test A 52
Selection Test B 55

"The Fall of the House of Usher" and **"The Raven"** by Edgar Allan Poe

Vocabulary and Reading Warm-ups 58
Literary Analysis: Single Effect 62
Reading Strategy: Breaking Down Long Sentences 63
Vocabulary Builder 64
Grammar and Style: Coordinate Adjectives 65
Support for Writing Lesson 66
Support for Extend Your Learning 67
Enrichment: Film Version of Edgar Allan Poe Stories 68
Selection Test A 69
Selection Test B 72

"The Minister's Black Veil" by Nathaniel Hawthorne

Vocabulary and Reading Warm-ups 75
Literary Analysis: Parable 79
Reading Strategy: Drawing Inferences About Meeting 80
Vocabulary Builder 81
Grammar and Style: Varying Sentence Openers 82
Support for Writing Lesson 83
Support for Extend Your Learning 84
Enrichment: Art 85
Selection Test A 86
Selection Test B 89

Benchmark Test 3 92

Diagnostic Test 4 98

from *Moby-Dick* by Herman Melville

Vocabulary and Reading Warm-ups 101
Literary Analysis: Symbol 105
Reading Strategy: Recognizing Symbols 106
Vocabulary Builder 107
Grammar and Style: Agreement With Collective Nouns 108
Support for Writing Lesson 109
Support for Extend Your Learning 110
Enrichment: Art 111
Selection Test A 112
Selection Test B 115

from *Nature*, from *Self-Reliance*, "The Snowstorm," and "Concord Hymn" by Ralph Waldo Emerson

Vocabulary and Reading Warm-ups 118
Literary Analysis: Transcendentalism 122
Reading Strategy: Challenging the Text 123
Vocabulary Builder 124
Grammar and Style: Varying Sentence Length 125
Support for Writing Lesson 126
Support for Extend Your Learning 127
Enrichment: Local Landmark 128
Selection Test A 129
Selection Test B 132
From the Scholar's Desk: Gretel Ehrlich 135
Listening and Viewing: Gretel Ehrlich 136

from *Walden* and from *Civil Disobedience* by Henry David Thoreau

Vocabulary and Reading Warm-ups 137
Literary Analysis: Style 141
Reading Strategy: Evaluating the Writer's Statement of Philosophy 142
Vocabulary Builder 143
Grammar and Style: Infinitives and Infinitive Phrases 144
Support for Writing Lesson 145
Support for Extend Your Learning 146
Enrichment: Social Studies 147
Selection Test A 148
Selection Test B 151

Emily Dickinson's Poetry

Vocabulary and Reading Warm-ups 154
Literary Analysis: Slant Rhyme 158
Reading Strategy: Analyzing Images 159
Vocabulary Builder 160
Grammar and Style: Gerunds 161
Support for Writing Lesson 162
Support for Extend Your Learning 163
Enrichment: Art 164
Selection Test A 165
Selection Test B 168

Walt Whitman's Poetry

Vocabulary and Reading Warm-ups 171
Literary Analysis: Free Verse 175
Reading Strategy: Inferring the Poet's Attitude 176
Vocabulary Builder 177
Grammar and Style: Pronoun-Antecedent Agreement 178
Support for Writing Lesson 179
Support for Extend Your Learning 180
Enrichment: Science 181
Selection Test A 182
Selection Test B 185

Writing About Literature: Compare and Contrast Literary Trends 188

Writing About Literature: Varying Sentence Length and Structure 189

Writing Workshop: Narration: Reflective Essay 190

Writing Workshop: Vary Sentences 191

Spelling: Proofreading Practice 192

Communications Workshop: Analyzing Media 193

Suggestions for Further Reading 194

Benchmark Test 4 195

Answers 201

Unit 3 Concept Map

The Big Picture: A Growing Nation
Nineteenth-Century (1800–1870)

Name: _____
Starting Date: _____
Ending Date: _____

Elements and Techniques

- Symbol/Style
- Meter/Rhyme/ Free Verse
- Description
- Point of View/ Single Effect

which are demonstrated in these selections:

Characteristics of the Period and Its Literature

In a nation of individuals, writers chart the individual's quest for self-realization.

Early poets follow European models, but Whitman and Dickinson create new forms.

The nation expands westward, inspiring writers to depict America's beauty.

Short stories of the period range from the picturesque to the hair-raising.

Meeting regularly in New England, writers champion a truly American literature.

Transcendentalists' optimism reflects new national self-confidence.

Transcendentalists celebrate the individual and see unity in all living things.

Anti-transcendentalists explore the dark side of the human psyche and of the Puritan tradition.

which are demonstrated in these selections:

- national self-confidence after decades of independence
- the New England Flowering
- Transcendentalism
- popular democracy

as shown in these selections

and demonstrates the cultural influence of

Forms and Movements

Transcendentalism

Parable

which are demonstrated in these selections:

- exact rhyme
- slant rhyme
- free verse
- diction
- parallelism

Focus on Literary Forms:

- Analyzing Images in—
- Inferring the Poet's Attitude in

Poetry

includes the elements

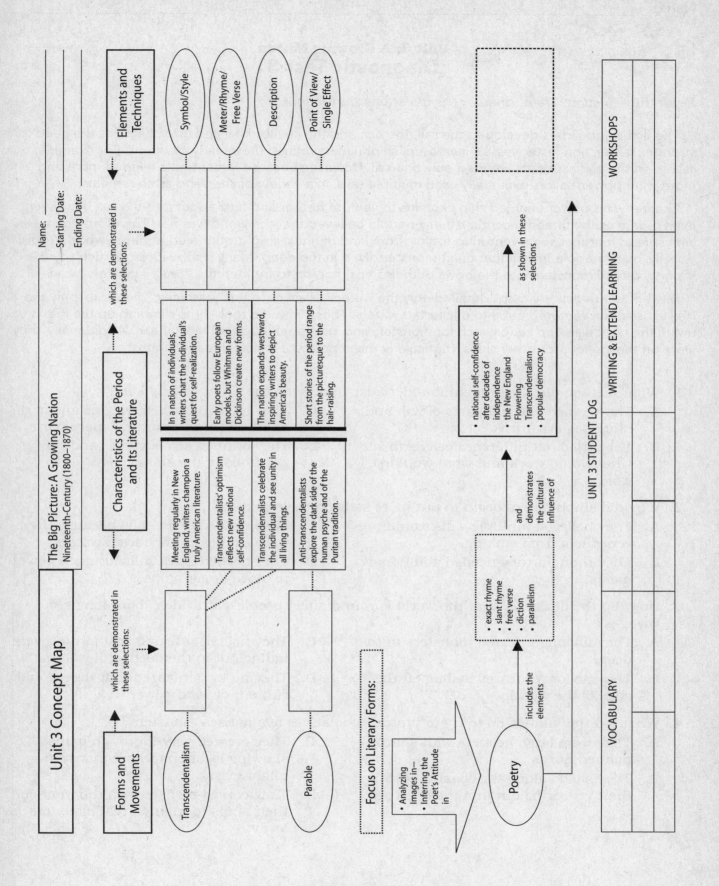

UNIT 3 STUDENT LOG

VOCABULARY	WRITING & EXTEND LEARNING	WORKSHOPS

1

Unit 3: A Growing Nation
Diagnostic Test 3

Read the selection. Then, answer the questions that follow.

The first shipbuilders developed the sail, the oar, and the keel by trial and error. Later, as the need for stronger, larger, and faster vessels increased, shipbuilders refined these early creations. For example, sailors on the earliest boats unfurled only one sail. However, because larger boats needed more and more wind power, sailors eventually used multiple sails, in a variety of sizes and arrangements.

Greater wind power enabled ship captains to venture further and further out into the sea. However, even as late as the fifteenth century, many people believed that the world was flat. Therefore, there was widespread fear that ships venturing too far from land might sail right off the edge of the world. Additionally, many people feared that giant monsters lived in the deep. Many shipbuilders, particularly the Vikings, carved monsters into the bows of their ships, hoping to frighten the "real" monsters away.

Most fifteenth-century maps detailed only the waters adjacent to the coastlines. Therefore, only the bravest seamen ventured out into uncharted waters. Those who did took turns climbing up the masts to unfurl the giant sails and keep watch for monsters and any hopeful signs of land ahead. Additionally, they were on the lookout for other ships, particularly those posing a critical threat—pirates!

1. What method did the first shipbuilders use to develop the sail, oar, and keel?
   A. They copied skeletal parts of fish and other sea creatures.
   B. They tried out different designs to see what would work and what wouldn't work.
   C. They took apart their wagons and carts and built boats from the spare parts.
   D. They studied sea currents and the positions of the stars.

2. Why did shipbuilders begin to put more sails on their boats?
   A. They believed multiple sails would prevent them from sinking.
   B. They thought they needed additional masts.
   C. They needed extra sails because they were sailing in uncharted waters.
   D. They needed extra sails for more power to move larger ships.

3. How did the discovery that the world is round affect people's attitudes about long sea voyages?
   A. They no longer feared monsters in the deep.
   B. They no longer feared sailing off the edge of the world.
   C. They no longer feared that pirates were hiding out in the deep, still waters.
   D. They no longer feared that they would run out of wind power.

4. What did the Vikings do to try to protect themselves against sea monsters?
   A. They wore large helmets with sharp, pointed horns.
   B. They sailed along the coastlines rather than venturing out into the open seas.
   C. They created very thorough maps, showing locations where monsters might exist.
   D. They carved monsters on the fronts of their ships to frighten real monsters away.

5. According to the selection, what was true about most fifteenth-century sea maps?
   A. They were created by the Vikings.
   B. They showed only the areas that were along the coastlines.
   C. They were created by pirates who sailed in the Mediterranean Sea.
   D. They showed the edge of the world.

6. According to the selection, why did it take courage to sail into uncharted waters?
   A. The seamen had to be willing to be away from home for as long as two or three years.
   B. The seamen had to be willing to withstand Viking attacks.
   C. The seamen had to be willing to sail into unknown, unmapped areas.
   D. The seamen had to be willing to sail very fast, with multiple sails and strong wind power.

7. Why did seamen use the masts as lookout stations?
   A. From the tops of the masts, they could see far away in all directions.
   B. From the tops of the masts, they could unfurl the sails.
   C. The masts were equipped with radar, sonar, and other useful devices.
   D. The seamen's maps were kept in cabinets at the tops of the masts.

Read the selection. Then, answer the questions that follow.

Elizabethan England often suggests images of the Royal Court with lavish costumes, meals, and entertainment. In that romantic picture, music fills the air while lords and ladies stroll through formal gardens or feast at long banquet tables filled with delicious food. But that image was accurate only for the privileged few. Outside the castle, life for most people was often grim.

The city of London was incredibly dirty and overcrowded. Houses were built close together on dark, airless lanes. People dumped their garbage into a gutter that ran down the center of each street. There the garbage stayed until a rainstorm finally washed it away.

The bubonic plague was a constant threat, spreading rapidly through entire neighborhoods. It killed so many people that it became known as "black death." Although it was spread by rats with fleas, officials mistakenly blamed stray dogs. Therefore, whenever an outbreak occurred, dogs were destroyed. This folly allowed the rats to multiply and did nothing to control the epidemic.

Poverty, crime, and lack of nutrition made life tough for most people. There were basically two levels of society—the very rich and the very poor. Very few people managed to rise above poverty to a level of comfort that in modern times has become the large middle class.

8. What is the meaning of *lavish*, as it is used in the phrase *lavish costumes, meals, and entertainment*?
   A. colorful
   B. casual
   C. fine
   D. delicious

9. According to the selection, how was life at court different from the life of most people?
   A. The people at court had luxuries that most people didn't have.
   B. Most people had more luxuries than the people who were at court.
   C. The privileged few had fewer luxuries than those of the majority.
   D. The people at court had a grim, overcrowded life.

10. Based on the selection, which statement is most accurate about London neighborhoods?
   A. The houses were made of bricks or lumber.
   B. The neighborhoods smelled of garbage and filth.
   C. It rained almost every day.
   D. There were formal gardens at the sides of the streets.

11. According to the selection, what is bubonic plague?
   A. a proclamation concerning the laws of the land
   B. a raging storm that can cause terrible damage to buildings and property
   C. terrible poverty
   D. a deadly disease

12. What mistake did officials make regarding bubonic plague?
   A. They thought that it was spread by stray cats.
   B. They thought that it was spread by stray dogs.
   C. They thought that it was spread by fleas.
   D. They thought that it was spread by rotting garbage.

13. Why did the officials' mistaken actions allow rats to multiply?
   A. Without fleas, the rats were healthier.
   B. The rats were left alone to multiply.
   C. The rats had plenty of garbage to eat.
   D. The rats thrived in dark, airless lanes.

14. According to the selection, what was true about Elizabethan England?
   A. Everyone suffered because of poverty and crime.
   B. There were three levels of society—the rich, the laborers, and the poor.
   C. There were two levels of society—the rich and the poor.
   D. With hard work, many people could rise to a level of comfort known as the middle class.

15. According to the selection, how is modern England different from Elizabethan England?
   A. There are no castles in modern England.
   B. There is no poverty in modern England.
   C. There is no middle class in modern England.
   D. There is a large middle class in modern England.

Name _____ Date _____

Unit 3 Introduction
Names and Terms to Know

A. DIRECTIONS: *Match each name or term on the left with its fact on the right. Write the letter of the fact on the line before the name or term it defines.*

Names and Terms

___ 1. Alexis de Tocqueville

___ 2. Louisiana Purchase

___ 3. Sacajawea

___ 4. War of 1812

___ 5. Gold Rush

___ 6. Seneca Falls Convention

___ 7. Romanticism

___ 8. Transcendentalism

Facts

A. addition of land to America during the presidency of Thomas Jefferson that doubled the nation's size

B. westward movement characterized by the discovery of gold in the West in 1849; Americans hurried there in hopes of becoming rich

C. gathering held to discuss and promote the idea of rights for women

D. artistic movement in Europe and America during the nineteenth century; writers focused on imagination and intuition rather than reason and fact

E. guide who led Lewis and Clark on their journey across the Northwest Territories

F. person who traveled all over America and reported on its spirit and energy in *Democracy in America*

G. three-year battle fought between the British and the Americans; Americans were protecting their interests on land and at sea

H. philosophical and artistic movement that developed after 1840; focused on matters beyond concrete understanding

B. DIRECTIONS: *Write an additional fact about each of the following names and terms.*

1. Alexis de Tocqueville: _____

_____

2. Sacajawea: _____

_____

3. Seneca Falls Convention: _____

_____

4. Transcendentalism: _____

_____

Unit 3 Introduction
Focus Questions

DIRECTIONS: *Use the hints below to help you answer the Focus Questions. You will find all of the information in the Unit Introduction in your textbook.*

1. In what ways did the growth in the size of the United States during this period affect the nation's view of itself?

   Hint: Think about the geographical changes in the nation as you examine the map on p. 246 _____

   _____

   _____

   Hint: How did America behave in relation to the other nations in the world? _____

   _____

   _____

2. As a result of growing prosperity, what challenges confronted the United States in the mid-nineteenth century?

   Hint: How did the physical growth of the nation create new challenges? _____

   _____

   _____

   Hint: How did industrialization affect people? _____

   _____

   _____

3. In what ways does the literature of this period reflect the country's expansion?

   Hint: Think about the focus of the Romanticists and the Transcendentalists. _____

   _____

   _____

   Hint: Which writers best reflect the expansive, hopeful nature of the young nation, as well as the challenges it faced? _____

   _____

   _____

Vocabulary Warm-up Word Lists

Study these words from the selection. Then, complete the activities.

Word List A

consequence [KAHN suh kwents] *n.* result, effect
  As a <u>consequence</u> of your carelessness, we have no more water.

elapsed [ee LAPST] *v.* passed, went by
  Five minutes <u>elapsed</u> before they returned.

indifference [in DIF fer uhnts] *n.* not caring; lack of interest
  They showed <u>indifference</u> and paid no attention to the screaming fans.

meager [MEE ger] *adj.* very thin; inadequate
  Such a <u>meager</u> salary for this tough job is unfair.

notorious [no TOR ee us] *adj.* having a bad reputation; infamous
  That government was <u>notorious</u> for corruption and injustice.

prior [PRY er] *adj.* previous; coming before
  Her <u>prior</u> service in the military helped her get the job.

prone [PROHN] *adj.* inclined (to)
  Because he did everything so fast, he was <u>prone</u> to having accidents.

zeal [ZEEL] *n.* great enthusiasm; passion
  The candidate wanted campaign workers with plenty of <u>zeal</u>.

Word List B

contradiction [kahn truh DIK shun] *n.* something opposite; denial
  This evidence is a <u>contradiction</u> of what we thought was true.

disclosed [dis KLOHZD] *v.* showed, revealed
  The witness finally <u>disclosed</u> the fact that he had not been there.

precaution [pree KAW shun] *n.* care taken in advance
  We took every <u>precaution</u> to avoid running out of supplies.

prevalent [PRE vuh lent] *adj.* widely existing; most common
  The <u>prevalent</u> attitude around here is that the mayor is doing a good job.

squeamish [SKWEEM ish] *adj.* easily nauseated or offended
  If you are <u>squeamish</u>, you may want to avoid this graphic documentary.

steadfastly [STED fast lee] *adv.* with firmness; without changing
  The soldier remained at his post <u>steadfastly</u> throughout the night.

strenuous [STREN yoo us] *adj.* demanding great effort or energy
  Before <u>strenuous</u> exercise, be sure to warm up and stretch.

uppermost [UP per mohst] *adj.* highest; first
  Protecting ourselves from danger was <u>uppermost</u> in our minds.

"The Devil and Tom Walker" by Washington Irving
Vocabulary Warm-up Exercises

Exercise A *Fill in the blanks, using each word from Word List A only once.*

Even though organized recycling has been around for a number of years, many people

still show nothing but [1] _____ to it. So, in order to inject some renewed

[2] _____ into this important movement, our community has just

held a "Pay Attention to Recycling" campaign. People who had been making only a

[3] _____ effort to recycle bottles, cans, and paper were bombarded

with ads, fliers, door-to-door visits, and even legal pressure. Businesses that were

[4] _____ for waste and individuals who were [5] _____ to

just throwing things away did seem to respond positively. [6] _____ to the

campaign, the recycling center was seldom busy; after the campaign, it was bustling. As

a [7] _____, before one month had [8] _____, our commu-

nity was a cleaner and more environmentally friendly place.

Exercise B *Decide whether each statement is true or false. Circle T or F, and explain your answer.*

1. If two statements agree, one of them is clearly a <u>contradiction</u>.
   T / F _____

2. If winning is <u>uppermost</u> in your mind, you are a fierce competitor.
   T / F _____

3. A nurse who stays at a patient's side all night does her job <u>steadfastly</u>.
   T / F _____

4. If you have no problem eating squishy, slimy things, you are not <u>squeamish</u>.
   T / F _____

5. Buckling your seatbelt is a <u>precaution</u> that can save your life.
   T / F _____

6. If a sport is too <u>strenuous</u> for you, you play it easily every day.
   T / F _____

7. If, in a mystery novel, a letter <u>disclosed</u> the truth, then the letter kept the truth hidden.
   T / F _____

8. If a disease is <u>prevalent</u> among a group of people, no one has it.
   T / F _____

"The Devil and Tom Walker" by Washington Irving
Reading Warm-up A

Read the following passage. Pay special attention to the underlined words. Then, read it again, and complete the activities. Use a separate sheet of paper for your written answers.

Salmagundi, or The Whim-Whams and Opinions of Launcelot Langstaff, was a collection of satires produced in twenty pamphlets during 1807–08. The writers were Washington Irving, his brother William, and the novelist James Kirke Paulding. These young men wrote with great zeal and enthusiasm under a variety of names, including Will Wizard and Anthony Evergreen. They took on the tastes, attitudes, and behavior of New York society. Their targets ranged from politics to fashion, from the notorious and celebrated to the merely harmless and obscure.

The pieces in *Salmagundi* were full of whimsy and satire, and they were prone to caricature, tending to exaggerate their portraits. They often created humor by pretending to have learning that they obviously did not really possess, claiming "serious truths conveyed in every paper." *Salmagundi* offered sophisticated and genuinely funny writing in post-colonial America, when elegance was scarce and the production of really fine humorous writing was also still quite meager.

The writers of *Salmagundi* never seemed to articulate any detailed political or aesthetic principles. As a consequence, the overall effect of the satires was very scattered and random. In fact, it was just like a salmagundi—a mixed salad of chicken, veal, anchovies, onions, and oil and lemon dressing. Some critics see this attitude as particularly American—practical, on-the-spot satire, dealing with whatever came to mind. It was the approach of a society that was still unsure of itself. It was the stance of a nation still trying to establish its identity with such a short time having elapsed since the Revolution.

What *Salmagundi* did have was vitality. It projected the high spirit that assumes the worst crime is indifference, not caring at all. Before this display of extravagant humor—that is, prior to *Salmagundi*—Washington Irving was a young law student, fond of theater and music. After *Salmagundi*, he was a writer.

1. Circle the word that means the same as zeal. Name something that you do with **zeal**.

2. Underline the words that help explain notorious. Name something for which a person can be **notorious**.

3. Circle the words that mean prone. Use *prone* in a sentence of your own.

4. Underline the word that helps explain meager. Name something of which you can have a **meager** supply.

5. Circle the words that identify the consequence of not articulating principles. Describe one possible **consequence** of winning the lottery.

6. Underline the words that tell what elapsed. How many hours have *elapsed* since your last English class?

7. Circle the words that explain indifference. Name something toward which you feel **indifference**.

8. Underline the word that means the same as prior. Name something you do **prior** to having lunch.

Name _____   Date _____

"The Devil and Tom Walker" by Washington Irving
Reading Warm-up B

Read the following passage. Pay special attention to the underlined words. Then, read it again, and complete the activities. Use a separate sheet of paper for your written answers.

The mythology of the American wilderness has engaged scholars for decades. What role did the great expanse of nature, especially the forest, play in the American imagination? One fact has been <u>disclosed</u> by the many analyses of the literature and history of eighteenth-century and nineteenth-century America. These studies reveal that the wilderness was undoubtedly a <u>contradiction</u> that embodied opposing forces, symbolized opposing ideas, and unleashed opposing impulses.

On the one hand, the wilderness was a refuge, a flourishing paradise to which Europeans fled in order to escape difficult, even fatal, circumstances. Arriving from lands where poverty existed widely and religious persecution was <u>prevalent</u>, those early Americans imagined the wilderness as a place of beauty, freedom, and opportunity. What was <u>uppermost</u> in their minds was the chance the wilderness provided to create their own lives. To them, the natural wilderness was a new Eden and they were all Adams and Eves.

On the other hand, the wilderness was also a place of danger, an environment of evil itself, and <u>strenuous</u> efforts were necessary simply to ensure survival in it. Americans had to take every <u>precaution</u>, exercise every care, when venturing into the forest, and anyone who was too <u>squeamish</u>, too sensitive about what might be found there, was probably better off staying in town or returning to Europe. The forest was huge and dark, uncivilized and unforgiving.

So the American wilderness grew in the imagination as both divine and diabolical. It was a place of delight and independence, and, at the same time, an abode of crime, sin, and death. It was a place that offered freedom, but it also demanded that a man or woman face it <u>steadfastly</u>, with physical hardiness, moral courage, and firm resolve. The wilderness was a place where an American might create his identity, meet his doom—or both.

1. Underline the word that helps explain <u>disclosed</u>. Name a fact *disclosed* recently in the news.

2. Circle the words that help explain <u>contradiction</u>. Identify the prefix in *contradiction* that indicates two things being "against" each other.

3. Underline the words that help explain <u>prevalent</u>. Identify an attitude you think is *prevalent* in your school.

4. Name an antonym for *uppermost*.

5. Explain why the early Americans' efforts had to be <u>strenuous</u>. What is a synonym for *strenuous*?

6. Circle the word that means <u>precaution</u>. Name a common *precaution* that people take in their daily lives.

7. Circle the words that explain <u>squeamish</u>. Name something about which many people are *squeamish*.

8. Underline the words that help explain <u>steadfastly</u>. Describe a situation in which someone acts *steadfastly*.

Name _____ Date _____

Literary Analysis: Omniscient Point of View

The narrator who stands outside the action and relates many characters' thoughts and feelings is called the **omniscient point of view.** *Omniscient* means "all-knowing."

DIRECTIONS: *On the lines provided, identify what the omniscient narrator tells the reader about a character's thoughts and feelings in each passage.*

1. What these conditions were may easily be surmised, though Tom never disclosed them publicly. They must have been very hard, for he required time to think of them, and he was not a man to stick at trifles where money was in view.

   _____

   _____

2. He [Tom] was not prone to let his wife into his confidence; but as this was an uneasy secret, he willingly shared it with her.

   _____

   _____

3. All her [Tom's wife's] avarice was awakened at the mention of hidden gold, and she urged her husband to comply with the black man's [Devil's] terms and secure what would make them wealthy for life.

   _____

   _____

4. However Tom might have felt disposed to sell himself to the Devil, he was determined not to do so to oblige his wife; so he flatly refused, out of the mere spirit of contradiction.

   _____

   _____

5. At length she [Tom's wife] determined to drive the bargain on her own account, and if she succeeded, to keep all the gain to herself.

   _____

   _____

6. The old blacklegs [the Devil] played shy, for whatever people may think, he is not always to be had for calling for: he knows how to play his cards when pretty sure of his game.

   _____

   _____

"The Devil and Tom Walker" by Washington Irving
Reading Strategy: Infer Cultural Attitudes

The characters in "The Devil and Tom Walker" are American colonists living in New England in the late 1720s and early 1730s. The dialogue, the narrator's comments about the characters, and the events that the characters experience help the reader **to infer cultural attitudes** of the period. Of course, some of these influences and attitudes are often exaggerated in Irving's satirical story. Nevertheless, readers do get a picture of colonial life in the New England of Tom Walker's day.

DIRECTIONS: *On the basis of each passage that follows, draw an inference about the ethical, social, and cultural influences and attitudes of New Englanders, or American colonists in general, in the 1720s and 1730s. Write the inference on the lines provided.*

1. Tom Walker . . . had a wife as miserly as himself: they were so miserly that they even conspired to cheat each other . . . many and fierce were the conflicts that took place about what ought to have been common property.

   _____

   _____

   _____

2. "I [the Devil] amuse myself by presiding at the persecutions of Quakers and Anabaptists; I am the great patron and prompter of slave dealers, and the grandmaster of the Salem witches."

   _____

   _____

   _____

3. About the year 1727, just at the time that earthquakes were prevalent in New England, and shook many tall sinners down upon their knees. . . .

   _____

   _____

   _____

4. Such was the end of Tom Walker and his ill-gotten wealth. Let all griping money brokers lay this story to heart.

   _____

   _____

   _____

Name _____ Date _____

"The Devil and Tom Walker" by Washington Irving
Vocabulary Builder

Using the Prefix *ex-*

A. DIRECTIONS: *The prefix* ex- *often means "out." Choose a word from the box to complete each sentence.*

exhale	extract	export	extrovert	exoskeleton	extricate

1. If you ship a product out of the country, you _____ it.
2. An _____ is an outgoing person.
3. When you breathe out, you _____.
4. An insect's outer shell is called an _____.
5. When you pull out a tooth, you _____ it.
6. If you get out of trouble, you _____ yourself from a tricky situation.

Using the Word List

avarice	usurers	extort	ostentation	parsimony

B. DIRECTIONS: *The following sentences are missing two words. On the line before each number, write the letter of the pair of terms that best completes each sentence.*

____ 1. He was a _____ who tried to _____ money.
    A. criminal—extort   C. avarice—treasure
    B. usurer—give   D. extortionist—donate

____ 2. Her _____ was awakened when she heard about the _____.
    A. husband—ostentation   C. avarice—treasure
    B. dog—usurer   D. parsimony—earthquake

____ 3. The house was _____, a monument to _____.
    A. loving—avarice   C. extorted—love
    B. bright—parsimony   D. lavish—ostentation

____ 4. The _____ was evidence of her _____.
    A. mouse—avarice   C. small portion—parsimony
    B. usurer—intelligence   D. tasteful decor—ostentation

____ 5. The _____ collected the _____ that was due.
    A. extortionist—video   C. child—avarice
    B. teacher—parsimony   D. usurer—fee

"The Devil and Tom Walker" by Washington Irving
Grammar and Style: Adjective Clauses

A subordinate clause is one that cannot stand alone as a sentence. An **adjective clause,** also called a relative clause, is a subordinate clause that adds information about a noun or pronoun. It is generally introduced by a relative pronoun: *who, whom, whose, which, that.*

Tom, *who had been picking his way through the forest,* met a stranger.
The stranger *that he met* was the devil.

A. PRACTICE: *Underline the adjective clause in each sentence.*

1. Many and fierce were the conflicts that took place.

2. The swamp was thickly grown with great gloomy pines and hemlocks, which made it dark at noonday.

3. Tom had long been picking his way cautiously through this treacherous forest; stepping from tuft to tuft of rushes and roots, which afforded precarious footholds among deep sloughs.

4. Here they had thrown up a kind of fort, which they had looked upon as almost impregnable, and had used as a place of refuge for their squaws and children.

5. On the bark of the tree was scored the name of Deacon Peabody, an eminent man, who had waxed wealthy by driving shrewd bargains with the Indians.

B. Writing Application: *Complete each sentence so that it contains an adjective clause. In some sentences, the relative pronoun is already provided.*

1. She greatly admired her teacher, who _____

_____

2. The man felt compassion for the stranger, whose _____

_____

3. They were astounded by the action, which _____

_____

4. He was captivated by the child, whose _____

_____

5. She pointed at the statue that _____

_____

"The Devil and Tom Walker" by Washington Irving
Support for Writing

As you prepare to write an updated **retelling** of "The Devil and Tom Walker," enter information in the chart below. Remember that you want to communicate the same message but with different plot elements and details about the characters. Also remember to use modern examples of food, clothing, and current events.

Modern Retelling of "The Devil and Tom Walker"	
New Title	
Characters with new details: Tom Tom's wife The Devil	
New plot elements: Where Tom and Wife live Where they meet Devil What happens with characters How story ends	
Modern day references: Clothing Food Current events	

On a separate page, write a draft of your updated version of the Irving tale. When you revise your draft, be sure you have updated the elements of the nineteenth-century story to reflect today's world.

"The Devil and Tom Walker" by Washington Irving
Support for Extend Your Learning

Listening and Speaking

As you prepare a **reenactment** of the meeting between Tom's wife and the Devil, use the following tips:

- Write dialogue to show what action might take place between the two characters.
- Choose a classmate to perform the scene with you.

Practice the scene with your classmate. Then, present it to the class. You might want to switch roles and present the scene twice.

Research and Technology

In preparation for your **essay** on the works that are based on the Faust legend, do research on the Internet and in the library. Enter your findings into the chart below.

The Faust Legend	Operas based on legend

Plays based on legend	Broadway musical based on legend

On a separate page, write your essay on the influence the Faust legend has had on other kinds of literary works.

Name _____   Date _____

"The Devil and Tom Walker" by Washington Irving
Enrichment: Narrative Point of View

Film directors use many techniques to tell their stories. They may shoot a scene using an unusual camera angle, filters, or animation. They may add a voice-over, music, or sound effects to a particular scene. They may even film part of a scene using a "fantasy" sequence, where the audience "sees" objects as if through the character's mind. If you think about films you have seen, you could list other techniques film directors use.

DIRECTIONS: *Choose three scenes from "The Devil and Tom Walker" that you might portray in a film. First, briefly describe each scene. Then, describe the techniques you might use to film each scene, keeping the viewpoint of the omniscient narrator. Write your answers on the lines provided.*

Scene 1: _____

_____

Techniques for filming: _____

_____

_____

_____

Scene 2: _____

_____

Techniques for filming: _____

_____

_____

_____

Scene 3: _____

_____

Techniques for filming: _____

_____

_____

_____

"The Devil and Tom Walker" by Washington Irving
Selection Test A

Critical Reading *Identify the letter of the choice that best answers the question.*

____ 1. Which answer choice shows that the third-person omniscient point of view is used in "The Devil and Tom Walker"?

    I. The narrator is not a character in the story.

    II. Tom's and his wife's feelings are both described.

    III. Tom argues with the Devil about the buried money.

    IV. The narrator comments on the death of Captain Kidd.

    A. I, II, III

    B. II, III, IV

    C. I, III, IV

    D. I, II, IV

____ 2. Based on "The Devil and Tom Walker," what was one belief of the New England Puritans during this time period?

    A. justice for Native Americans

    B. witches and demons

    C. accepting all religions

    D. giving the vote to women

____ 3. In "The Devil and Tom Walker," how does the writer show that Tom's wife is meant to represent many women rather than one specific woman?

    A. Her character has no name.

    B. She is a strong woman.

    C. She is a Puritan.

    D. Her character is fearless.

____ 4. In "The Devil and Tom Walker," why does Tom's wife go off into the forest with her best silver?

    A. She hopes to sell it and leave Tom.

    B. She is taking a gift to a relative.

    C. She wants to deal with the Devil.

    D. She plans to trade it for food.

____ 5. Based on "The Devil and Tom Walker," which of the following beliefs did the Puritans of this time hold?

    A. Husbands and wives are considered to be equal.

    B. The Devil can take sometimes a human form.

    C. You can always tell who is a respected businessman.

    D. Those who say loud prayers are the truest worshippers.

____ 6. Based on Tom's behavior in "The Devil and Tom Walker," which of these groups did Irving likely support?

    A. Salem witches

    B. slave-traders

    C. abolitionists

    D. money-lenders

____ 7. What most likely happens to Tom at the end of "The Devil and Tom Walker"?

    A. He rides off to escape the anger of people to whom he loaned money.

    B. The Devil kidnaps him to get his money and horses.

    C. The Devil ends his life and takes him to hell.

    D. He takes his riches and retires to another town.

____ 8. Which of these sentences about "The Devil and Tom Walker" reflects the third-person omniscient point of view?

    A. He saw a dark, coarsely dressed man sitting on a log.

    B. Tom hoped to spite his wife and she hoped to outwit him.

    C. Tom got rich by lending money to the townspeople.

    D. I saw a name written on the bark of the huge tree.

Vocabulary and Grammar

____ 9. In which sentence is the meaning of the word *avarice* expressed?

    A. The Devil carried Tom off forever on his black horse.

    B. Tom and his wife were equally greedy for riches.

    C. The other worshippers suspected Tom's false prayers.

    D. Tom's wife went into the woods and did not return.

____ 10. Which of the following sentences uses an adjective clause?

    A. "This inlet allowed a facility to bring the money in a boat secretly and at night . . ."

    B. "He was exceedingly surprised, having neither heard nor seen anyone approach . . ."

    C. "Tom had long been picking his way cautiously through this treacherous forest . . ."

    D. ". . . a mighty rich man of that name, who made a vulgar display of wealth . . ."

Essay

11. In literature, a one-dimensional character is a person who does not change his or her basic nature. Do you think Tom and his wife are one-dimensional characters who always act greedy in "The Devil and Tom Walker"? Why or why not? Write a brief essay to give your opinion. Support it with at least two examples from the story.

12. Do you think Tom Walker deserved his fate in "The Devil and Tom Walker," based on the kind of person he was and the job he held? Why or why not? Write a brief essay to explain your point of view. Use at least two examples from the story to support your opinion.

"The Devil and Tom Walker" by Washington Irving
Selection Test B

Critical Reading *Identify the letter of the choice that best completes the statement or answers the question.*

____ 1. The opening descriptions of the forest suggest that what Tom will find there will be
A. treacherous and malignant.
B. fortunate and useful.
C. hot-tempered and vengeful.
D. dull and depressing.

____ 2. Which of these details most clearly suggest that the figure Tom meets is the Devil?
A. His voice is hoarse and growling, and his hair is black.
B. His eyes are red, and he is covered with soot.
C. He is powerfully built and is holding an ax.
D. He wears rude, half-Indian garb and is sitting on a tree stump.

____ 3. What is the significance of Tom's finding most of the tall trees in the forest each "marked with the name of some great man of the colony"?
A. The townspeople carved great men's names on trees.
B. Landowners carved their names on trees on their property.
C. The men had carved their own names on the trees to ensure their fame.
D. Carved onto the trees in the Devil's forest are the names of those who made a deal with him.

____ 4. What seems to be Tom's prime motivation in agreeing to the Devil's terms?
A. the desire to spite his wife
B. gratitude for the Devil's involvement in his wife's disappearance
C. the desire to win the respect of the community
D. greed

____ 5. A main lesson of this story is that
A. greed and mean-spiritedness lead to misery.
B. husbands and wives should love each other.
C. prayer can erase all past sins.
D. great wealth can never produce happiness.

____ 6. The story implies that God expresses His disapproval of humans' sins by
A. ignoring their prayers.
B. making them poor.
C. causing natural disasters.
D. giving them nightmares.

____ 7. In what way is Tom Walker a one-dimensional character?
A. He has no personality traits.
B. He uses other people for his own gain.
C. He does not fear the Devil.
D. He symbolizes human greed and miserliness.

____ 8. It can be inferred from the story that New England Puritans of Tom Walker's day believed in
   A. many gods.
   B. witches and spirits.
   C. tolerance of all religious faiths.
   D. reincarnation.

____ 9. From the description of Tom's "violent" religious devotion, you can infer that New Englanders of the 1720s probably
   A. believed that loud and vehement prayer was the key to reaching Heaven.
   B. looked suspiciously on sudden and very public conversions.
   C. welcomed religious people of all faiths to their colony.
   D. were, like Tom, usually recent converts to openly devout Christianity.

____ 10. Which of these statements does *not* apply to an omniscient narrator?
   A. The narrator stands outside the story.
   B. The narrator provides the thoughts or feelings of many characters.
   C. The narrator may comment on events in the story.
   D. The narrator is a character in the story who refers to himself or herself with the first-person pronoun *I*.

____ 11. Which of these statements best demonstrates an omniscient narrator?
   A. Tom was walking through the forest.
   B. Tom's wife was tall and greedy.
   C. Mrs. Walker hoped that Tom would make the pact, but Tom would not agree, just to spite her.
   D. As Tom grew older, he began to worry about what would happen after he died.

____ 12. With which special-interest group of Irving's day does the story suggest Irving had the most sympathy?
   A. abolitionists
   B. New England shipbuilders
   C. Puritans
   D. bankers

____ 13. Which of these observations about the story stems from the use of an omniscient narrator?
   A. The narrator focuses on Tom's experiences.
   B. The narrator never tells us what happened to Tom's wife.
   C. The narrator makes clear the motives and desires of Tom and his wife.
   D. The narrator keeps the Devil shrouded in mystery.

Vocabulary and Grammar

____ 14. When the Devil says "You shall extort bonds," what is the meaning of the word *extort*?
   A. to write in legal language
   B. to sell by auction
   C. to break, unlink, or untie
   D. to obtain by threat or violence

____ 15. Which is the adjective clause in this sentence?

His reputation for a ready-moneyed man, who would lend money out for good consideration, soon spread abroad.

A. his reputation for a ready-moneyed man
B. for good consideration
C. who would lend money out for good consideration
D. soon spread abroad

____ 16. Which relationship best describes the italicized words in this sentence?

He built himself, as usual, a vast house, out of *ostentation*; but left the greater part of it unfinished and unfurnished, out of *parsimony*.

A. They are identical in meaning.
B. They are similar in meaning.
C. They are opposite in meaning.
D. There is no relationship.

____ 17. In suggesting that Tom's wife is guilty of the sin of *avarice*, the narrator is criticizing her
A. greed.
B. spitefulness.
C. violence.
D. tendency to bicker.

Essay

18. Which tree do you think is hit by the thunderbolt falling at the end of the story? In a brief essay, state your theory and then support it with information from the selection.

19. How does the use of an omniscient narrator affect this story? Analyze the effects in an essay that supports your general statements with examples from the selection. Be sure to include examples of scenes or dialogue that might *not* have been included if the story did not have an omniscient narrator.

20. At the end of the story, all of Tom's possessions disappear or are destroyed. Why do you think this happens? Offer your theory in an essay that uses information from the story to support your ideas.

Vocabulary Warm-up Word Lists

Study these words from the selections. Then, complete the activities.

Word List A

din [DIN] *n.* loud, continuous noise; uproar
After five hours, the <u>din</u> at the convention gave me a headache.

earnest [UR nest] *adj.* sincere; serious; intense
The <u>earnest</u> look on her face showed that she was not kidding.

mournful [MORN ful] *adj.* with great sorrow; expressing grief
At the funeral, the mood was quiet and <u>mournful</u>.

splendor [SPLEN der] *n.* magnificent glory; brightness
The wedding of the princess was a display of wealth and <u>splendor</u>.

strife [STRYF] *n.* bitter conflict; struggle
For ten years, that country has known only war and <u>strife</u>.

sublime [sub LYM] *adj.* noble; awe-inspiring
The aged composer produced <u>sublime</u> works that touched our hearts.

transfigured [trans FIG yerd] *v.* changed appearance or form
When the actress came out of the dressing room, she was <u>transfigured</u>.

waning [WAY ning] *v.* growing less; decreasing
The light of the <u>waning</u> moon was not enough to show us the road.

Word List B

efface [i FAYSS] *v.* erase completely
Workers were able to <u>efface</u> the writing that had covered the wall.

pensive [PEN siv] *adj.* quietly thoughtful
She sat in the corner, <u>pensive</u> and serious, staring out the window.

portent [POR tent] *n.* sign of something to come, especially a bad event
The dark clouds were clearly a <u>portent</u> of a storm.

reproach [ree PROHCH] *n.* expression of blame
Their looks of <u>reproach</u> showed that they knew it was his fault.

sustained [sus TAYND] *v.* supported; strengthened; comforted
Your friendship <u>sustained</u> me when I most needed help.

threadbare [THRED bayr] *adj.* worn down; shabby
The homeless man had only a <u>threadbare</u> coat to last all winter.

unfaltering [un FALL ter ing] *v.* not weakening, stumbling, or hesitating
With <u>unfaltering</u> courage, the team faced up to what they had to do.

vanquished [VANG kwisht] *v.* conquered; defeated
For years, the champions <u>vanquished</u> all opposition.

Poems by Henry Wadsworth Longfellow, William Cullen Bryant,
Oliver Wendell Holmes, and John Greenleaf Whittier

Vocabulary Warm-up Exercises

Exercise A *Fill in the blanks, using each word from Word List A only once.*

At the ceremony marking the anniversary of the victory, the people of the city filled the public square. The crowd was huge and noisy, and the [1] _____ even drowned out the band. The mayor was the main speaker, and, in serious and [2] _____ tones, he reminded everyone of the long and terrible [3] _____ that the nation had endured. He spoke of the way our heroes' efforts had [4] _____ our society, changing and improving it in many ways. He told us to rejoice and not to be [5] _____ for what we had lost, but to celebrate what we had achieved. He spoke of the glory and [6] _____ of what we have built, and encouraged us to keep our focus on achieving the [7] _____ ideals that inspire us. If we ever feel our devotion lessening and our enthusiasm [8] _____, the memory of that speech will raise our spirits again.

Exercise B *Answer the following questions with complete explanations.*

1. If you <u>efface</u> the name on a monument, can you still read it?

   _____

2. If someone is <u>pensive</u>, does he have something on his mind?

   _____

3. If a volcano rumbles, why would scientists consider that a <u>portent</u>?

   _____

4. If a friend looks at you with <u>reproach</u>, is she blaming you?

   _____

5. If you were selling a new coat, would you advertise it as <u>threadbare</u>?

   _____

6. If you <u>vanquished</u> your fear, would you still be terrified?

   _____

7. If your dog shows <u>unfaltering</u> obedience, does he sometimes disobey?

   _____

8. If a snack <u>sustained</u> you, how were you able to survive until dinnertime?

   _____

Poems by Henry Wadsworth Longfellow, William Cullen Bryant,
Oliver Wendell Holmes, and John Greenleaf Whittier

Reading Warm-up A

Read the following passage. Pay special attention to the underlined words. Then, read it again, and complete the activities. Use a separate sheet of paper for your written answers.

As the national tragedy of the Civil War raged, Henry Wadsworth Longfellow faced his own personal tragedy. In 1861 his second wife died, and grief overwhelmed him. Mournful, he was unable to write for month after month. The enormously popular author of *Hiawatha* and *The Courtship of Miles Standish* could produce nothing. Time passed, but his pain was not lessening and his emptiness was not waning. He knew he had to find a solution.

To refocus his mind and emotions, Longfellow resolved to translate Dante's *Divine Comedy*. He formed the Dante Club with poet James Russell Lowell, editor Charles Eliot Norton, doctor Oliver Wendell Holmes, and several others. Every Wednesday night, they would meet at Longfellow's house in Cambridge and discuss Longfellow's ongoing translation until late in the morning.

These brilliant and sensitive men realized that the journey taken by the great poet Dante in the *Commedia* was ideally suited to match the emotional journey that Longfellow needed to take. Longfellow felt his life had become an "inferno" of struggle and strife. He had to escape from that place where the din, the eternal noise, of suffering had become almost unbearable. Through the act of translation, Longfellow was able to travel with Dante through that pain up to a sublime vision of an awe-inspiring paradise.

Through his participation in literature, Longfellow transfigured himself. He changed his outlook on life and revitalized his creativity. Perhaps the splendor of his translation, its real glory, had its strongest source in his deep personal need, just as it did for Dante. Longfellow's intense passion and sincere idealism arose from an earnest desire to lift himself out of his own private inferno and reach a higher, better place.

1. Circle the words that explain <u>mournful</u>. Name two antonyms for *mournful*.

2. Underline the word that means <u>waning</u>. Name something for which enthusiasm can be *waning*.

3. Circle the word that explains <u>strife</u>. Use *strife* in a sentence of your own.

4. Underline the word that means <u>din</u>. Describe a situation in which you experienced a *din*.

5. Circle the word that means the same as <u>sublime</u>. Define *sublime* in your own words.

6. Underline the word that means <u>transfigured</u>. Explain how the root of *transfigured* shows it has something to do with form or appearance.

7. Circle the word that means <u>splendor</u>. Describe something that you think has *splendor*.

8. Underline the words that help explain <u>earnest</u>. Describe a situation in which someone is not *earnest*.

Poems by Henry Wadsworth Longfellow, William Cullen Bryant,
Oliver Wendell Holmes, and John Greenleaf Whittier

Reading Warm-up B

Read the following passage. Pay special attention to the underlined words. Then, read it again, and complete the activities. Use a separate sheet of paper for your written answers.

We usually think of the great nineteenth-century writers as gray-bearded old men, and we cannot imagine them as untried and uncertain teenagers. An anecdote of the young Longfellow can help <u>efface</u> that impression and wipe away that image.

On November 17, 1820, the *Portland Gazette* published a poem called "The Battle of Lovell's Pond," verses that retold a local legend and identified the author only as "Henry," although in fact the poet was the overjoyed thirteen-year-old Longfellow. To him, the poem was a triumph that <u>vanquished</u> his self-doubts. He had put himself out into the wide world for the first time, and, although he had told no one that he was the author, he felt optimistic about his future.

As it happened, Longfellow had been invited to the home of a friend for dinner that night, and his friend's father, the respected Judge Mellen, mentioned the poem he had read that morning. Not knowing that the author was sitting at his table, he scornfully called the poem "remarkably stiff," a <u>threadbare</u> fabric of words, ragged, full of holes, even "borrowed from some other source." Longfellow did not direct any words of <u>reproach</u> to the judge; he did not dare blame any well-educated and powerful adult. Silent and <u>pensive</u>, he simply sat and thought, and, after dinner, went home and cried himself to sleep, deciding that this was a <u>portent</u>, an omen of failure.

Yet the next day, and the next, and for the following days and years, the poet continued to write. After that inauspicious beginning, or because of it, his belief in himself became fierce, unwavering, and <u>unfaltering</u>. The sting of that criticism—and, more importantly, his response to it—<u>sustained</u> him throughout the years, supporting his resolve. Eventually, "Henry" became the best-selling poet in the English language.

1. Underline the words that mean **efface**. Name something that you believe time cannot **efface**.

2. Circle the word that helps explain **vanquished**. Name two synonyms for **vanquished**.

3. Underline the words that help explain **threadbare**. Use **threadbare** in a sentence.

4. Circle the word that explains **reproach**. Write a sentence that contains a **reproach**.

5. Underline the word that explains **pensive**. Describe the behavior of someone who appears **pensive**.

6. Circle the word that means **portent**. Name an event that could be considered a **portent**.

7. Circle the word that means **unfaltering**. Describe a situation in which someone behaves with **unfaltering** devotion.

8. Underline the word that helps explain **sustained**. Describe a situation in which someone's words or actions **sustained** you.

"The Tide Rises, The Tide Falls" by Henry Wadsworth Longfellow
"Thanatopsis" by William Cullen Bryant
"Old Ironsides" by Oliver Wendell Holmes
from **Snowbound** by John Greenleaf Whittier

Literary Analysis: Meter

The **meter** of a poem is the rhythmic pattern created by the arrangement of stressed and unstressed syllables. The basic unit of meter is the **foot**, which usually consists of one stressed syllable and one or more unstressed syllables. The most common foot in English-language poetry is the **iamb**, an unstressed syllable followed by a stressed syllable, as in the word *today'*.

The type and number of feet per line determine the poem's meter. For example, a pattern of three iambs per line is called **iambic trimeter**; four iambs per line, **iambic tetrameter**; five iambs per line, **iambic pentameter**. The process of analyzing a poem's meter is called **scansion**, or **scanning** the poem. Here are examples of scanned lines.

Iambic tetrameter: Beneath it rung the battle shout

Iambic pentameter: Let each new temple, nobler than the last

DIRECTIONS: *Scan the following stanza of "Old Ironsides" by marking the stressed and unstressed syllables. Then describe the metrical pattern of the poem on these lines:*

_____

_____

Oh, better that her shattered hulk

   Should sink beneath the wave;

Her thunders shook the mighty deep,

   And there should be her grave;

Nail to the mast her holy flag.

   Set every threadbare sail,

And give her to the god of storms,

   The lightning and the gale

"The Tide Rises, The Tide Falls" by Henry Wadsworth Longfellow
"Thanatopsis" by William Cullen Bryant
"Old Ironsides" by Oliver Wendell Holmes
from **Snowbound** by John Greenleaf Whittier

Reading Strategy: Summarize

Summarizing is a valuable way to check your reading comprehension. When you **summarize** something, you briefly state its main points and key details in your own words.

DIRECTIONS: *Summarize each stanza below on the lines provided.*

1. "Thanatopsis":

Yet not to thine eternal resting place
Shalt thou retire alone, nor couldst thou wish
Couch more magnificent. Thou shalt lie down
With patriarchs of the infant world—with kings,
The powerful of the earth—the wise, the good,
Fair forms, and hoary seers of ages past,
All in one mighty sepulcher.

_____

_____

_____

2. "Old Ironsides":

Oh, better that her shattered hulk
  Should sink beneath the wave;
Her thunders shook the mighty deep,
  And there should be her grave;
Nail to the mast her holy flag.
  Set every threadbare sail,
And give her to the god of storms,
  The lightning and the gale!

_____

_____

_____

"The Tide Rises, The Tide Falls" by Henry Wadsworth Longfellow
"Thanatopsis" by William Cullen Bryant
"Old Ironsides" by Oliver Wendell Holmes
from **Snowbound** by John Greenleaf Whittier
Vocabulary Builder

Using the Root *-patr-*

A. DIRECTIONS: *The word root -patr- or -pater- means "father" or, by extension, "fatherland."*
Keeping that in mind, write on the line the letter of the choice that best completes each item.

____ 1. If a social system is a *patriarchy*, who most likely heads a household?

  A. a male parent   C. an unwed mother

  B. a bachelor   D. a wise grandmother

____ 2. A *patrician* is a person of high social status. What do you think determined status in the society in which this word originated?

  A. elections   C. salary

  B. academic achievement   D. family background

Using the Word List

sepulcher	venerable	ominous	patriarch
pensive	effaced	querulous	

B. DIRECTIONS: *On the lines provided, rewrite each sentence below, substituting the correct word from the Word List in place of its italicized definition.*

1. The darkness that morning was a very *menacing* prophecy of the snow to come.

_____

2. The valleys were blanketed in a *thoughtful* quietness.

_____

3. The rooster looked indignant, and his call seemed almost *cranky*.

_____

4. The wise, the good, and everyone else are buried now in one mighty *tomb*.

_____

5. The ram ruled the flock of sheep like a biblical *father figure*.

_____

6. The letters on the monument were *erased* by time.

_____

7. The woods are old and *deserving of respect*.

_____

"The Tide Rises, The Tide Falls" by Henry Wadsworth Longfellow
"Thanatopsis" by William Cullen Bryant
"Old Ironsides" by Oliver Wendell Holmes
from *Snowbound* by John Greenleaf Whittier

Grammar and Style: Participles as Adjectives

A **participle** is a verb form that can act as an adjective. When it does, it generally answers the question *what kind?* or *which one?* about the noun or pronoun it modifies. **Present participles** are formed by adding -ing to a verb. In this sentence, the present participle *moaning* modifies the noun *boughs*:

The *moaning* boughs swayed.

Past participles are usually formed by adding -ed to a verb. If the verb already ends in silent *e*, you drop the *e* before adding -ed. In the following sentences, the past participle *sharpened* modifies the noun *face*, and the past participle *baffled* modifies the noun *wind*. Note that *baffled* is a predicate adjective following a linking verb, *seemed*.

I turned a *sharpened* face to the cold. The north wind seemed *baffled*.

Some past participles are formed irregularly. These irregular forms often end in *n* or *t*. In the following sentence, the irregular past participles *blown* and *burnt* both modify the noun *leaves*.

The leaves, *burnt* and *blown*, covered the ground.

A. PRACTICE: *For each sentence below, underline the participle being used as an adjective, and circle the noun or pronoun that it modifies. If it is a present participle, write* present *on the line before the number. If it is a past participle, write* past. *If the sentence contains no participles used as adjectives, write* none *on the line before the sentence.*

_____ 1. It seemed to tell of Pisa's leaning miracle.

_____ 2. The cock his lusty greeting said, and forth his speckled harem led.

_____ 3. We minded that the sharpest ear the buried brooklet could not hear.

_____ 4. Our own warm hearth seemed blazing free.

B. Writing Application: *For the first four items below, describe each noun with a past or present participle. For the next four items, turn each verb into a past or present participle and use it to describe a noun of your choice.*

Nouns

1. _____ book   3. _____ sky

2. _____ rain   4. _____ child

Verbs

5. to soothe _____   7. to burn _____

6. to conquer _____ 8. to drape _____

"The Tide Rises, The Tide Falls" by Henry Wadsworth Longfellow
"Thanatopsis" by William Cullen Bryant
"Old Ironsides" by Oliver Wendell Holmes
from **Snowbound** by John Greenleaf Whittier

Support for Writing

As you prepare to write your précis (a brief summary) of the selection from *Snowbound*, select the main ideas, images, and other details you will need. Focus on putting the ideas in order from the beginning of the poem to the end.

Précis of Selection from *Snowbound*		
Beginning **Images/Events/Feelings**	**Middle** **Images/Events/Feelings**	**End** **Images/Events/Feelings**

On a separate page, draft your summary of the selection. When you revise your work, be sure you have included only the main ideas and images from each part of the poem.

Name _____ Date _____

Support for Extend Your Learning

Listening and Speaking

As you rehearse a **dramatic reading** of Holmes's "Old Ironsides," keep these things in mind:

- Work to understand the text and meter.
- Use a tone and pace that are suited to the work.
- Present the poem in a way that will persuade and move the audience.

Now present your dramatic reading to the class. Ask your classmates to give constructive criticism of your performance.

Research and Technology

Refer to the painting on page 267 by Thomas Cole. Gather information from the Internet for an **oral presentation** about Thomas Cole and the Hudson River School of artists. Enter your findings in the chart below.

Thomas Cole/Hudson River School	
Thomas Cole/Basic Biography	
Thomas Cole/Artwork/Hudson River School	
Thomas Cole/Connection to Bryant	

Present your oral report to the class. Compare your findings about Cole's connection with Bryant to what other classmates have discovered.

Name _____ Date _____

Enrichment: Science

The curlew mentioned in "The Tide Rises, The Tide Falls" is a large, long-legged wading bird whose call is associated with the evening. Knowing information about subjects discussed in a poem or story often helps the reader interpret meaning. In this case, knowing that a curlew's call is associated with the evening helps to visualize the setting of the poem and establish mood.

DIRECTIONS: *Research the curlew and four other birds of the Northeast. Use encyclopedias, field guides, or ornithology texts. As you find facts about each bird, fill in the following chart, explaining how the facts can be used to help establish a mood.*

Bird	Facts	How Can Knowing This Information Help To Establish a Mood?
Curlew		

"The Tide Rises, The Tide Falls" by Henry Wadsworth Longfellow
"Thanatopsis" by William Cullen Bryant
"Old Ironsides" by Oliver Wendell Holmes
from **Snowbound** by John Greenleaf Whittier

Selection Test A

Critical Reading *Identify the letter of the choice that best answers the question.*

____ 1. When happens at twilight in "The Tide Rises, The Tide Falls"?
   A. the sky darkens
   B. the horses neigh
   C. the sun shines
   D. the day begins

____ 2. Which statement below is a good summary of "The Tide Rises, the Tide Falls"?
   A. The tide goes in and out every day without ending.
   B. The actions of nature erase the actions of humans.
   C. Travelers hurry to arrive before darkness falls.
   D. The tide signals the beginning of each day.

____ 3. In poetry, what is the arrangement of lines into stressed and unstressed syllables called?
   A. rhythm
   B. rhyme
   C. imagery
   D. meter

____ 4. According to the poet in "Thanatopsis," what will happen to his listeners after they die?
   A. They will be buried in kings' tombs.
   B. They will be buried far out at sea.
   C. They will become less bitter.
   D. They will become part of the earth.

____ 5. In the following lines from "Old Ironsides," which syllables are accented?
   Her deck, once red with heroes' blood, / Where knelt the vanquished foe,
   A. every first syllable
   B. every second syllable
   C. every third syllable
   D. every syllable

_____ 6. What kind of ship is "Old Ironsides"?
   A. a motorboat
   B. a sailboat
   C. a battleship
   D. a cruise ship

_____ 7. Which statement below is the best summary of these lines from "Old Ironsides"?
   Her deck, once red with heroes' blood, / Where knelt the vanquished foe, / When winds were hurrying o'er the flood, / And waves were white below, / No more shall feel the victor's tread, / Or know the conquered knee;—
   A. The blood of past battles will be washed off the ship by water.
   B. The ship will no longer see people battling on her deck.
   C. The ship was best in battle when the waves were high.
   D. The winners no longer stay on deck but are honored on shore.

_____ 8. What is the meter of the selection from *Snowbound*, which consists of four poetic feet, each one consisting of an unstressed and a stressed syllable?
   A. iambic pentameter
   B. free verse
   C. iambic tetrameter
   D. couplets

_____ 9. Which statement below is the best summary of these lines from *Snowbound*?
   And, when the second morning shone, / We looked upon a world unknown, / On nothing we could call our own. / Around the glistening wonder bent / The blue walls of the firmament, / No cloud above, no earth below— / A universe of sky and snow!
   A. The second night of snow destroyed everything we owned.
   B. The sky remained blue even while it was snowing.
   C. The snow made the world look new and different.
   D. When morning came, the sky turned blue again.

Vocabulary and Grammar

_____ 10. In which of the following is the meaning of *ominous* expressed?
   A. "Old Ironsides" had fought and won many a battle.
   B. The poet urges people to approach death with trust.
   C. The sky grew dark and a wind howled out of the west.
   D. The gentle snow covered the grave of the poet's child.

____ **11.** Which example uses a participle as an adjective that modifies a noun?
   A. "On whitewashed wall and sagging beam"
   B. "Beneath it rung the battle shout"
   C. "Comes a still voice—Yet a few days, and thee"
   D. "As night drew on, and, from the crest"

Essay

12. In "Thanatopsis," Bryant says to people who will eventually die, "Thou shalt lie down / With patriarchs of the infant world—with kings, / The powerful of the earth—the wise, the good, / Fair forms, and hoary seers of ages past . . ." What do you think he is saying to readers about what will happen to them after death? What does he seem to suggest about how humans might be valued in death, compared to how they are valued in life? Write a brief essay to express your opinion of this passage.

13. What attitude toward death do you think Bryant has, based on "Thanatopsis"? Is he afraid of death? How does he want his readers to view death? Write a brief essay giving your ideas about the poet's view of death. Use evidence from the poem to support your ideas.

"The Tide Rises, The Tide Falls" by Henry Wadsworth Longfellow
"Thanatopsis" by William Cullen Bryant
"Old Ironsides" by Oliver Wendell Holmes
from **Snowbound** by John Greenleaf Whittier

Selection Test B

Critical Reading *Identify the letter of the choice that best completes the statement or answers the question.*

_____ 1. In "The Tide Rises, The Tide Falls," when does the curlew call?
    A. dawn
    B. noon
    C. twilight
    D. midnight

_____ 2. Which statement best expresses the theme of "The Tide Rises, The Tide Falls"?
    A. Life and death are beyond human control.
    B. Human life is short, but nature is eternal.
    C. Humans, like nature itself, are resilient.
    D. Human emotions have no place in the natural world.

_____ 3. The title "Thanatopsis" means
    A. a vision of death.
    B. the process of decaying.
    C. a metamorphosis or transformation.
    D. a feeling of euphoria or well-being.

_____ 4. According to the speaker in "Thanatopsis," what will happen to him after death?
    A. His soul will go to heaven.
    B. His spirit will cease to exist.
    C. His body will be preserved in the earth.
    D. His body will become part of nature.

_____ 5. Bryant's line "Shall send his roots abroad, and pierce thy mold" is an example of iambic _____.
    A. trimeter
    B. tetrameter
    C. pentameter
    D. hexameter

_____ 6. "Old Ironsides" was the nickname of
    A. the *U.S.S. Constitution,* a War of 1812 battleship.
    B. the *Clermont,* an early steamship.
    C. the *Titanic,* a famous luxury liner.
    D. Oliver Wendell Holmes.

____ 7. Which of these qualities does Holmes's poem attribute to "Old Ironsides"?
   A. ruthlessness
   B. heroism
   C. holiness
   D. modesty

____ 8. Which of these statements best expresses the author's view in "Old Ironsides"?
   A. A remarkable national relic should be saved.
   B. Old ships are architectural treasures.
   C. Ships are the foundation of a country's defense.
   D. Older things are built better than newer things.

____ 9. The family in *Snowbound*
   A. was not prepared for the sudden snowfall.
   B. feared the isolation of being snowed in.
   C. suffered in the cold weather of the winter storm.
   D. enjoyed the solitude brought by the snowfall.

____ 10. Which choice below best summarizes these lines from *Snowbound*?
   A tunnel walled and overlaid / With dazzling crystal: we had read
   Of rare Aladdin's wondrous cave, / And to our own his name we gave. . . .

   A. The boys used crystals to build a tunnel in the snow.
   B. The boys recalled their readings as they built a walled tunnel.
   C. The boys built a tunnel overlaid with dazzling crystal and, having read of Aladdin's
      wondrous cave, gave their own tunnel the same name, calling it Aladdin's cave.
   D. The boys built a tunnel in the snow and named it after Aladdin's cave.

____ 11. Which of the following lines is *not* written in iambic terameter?
   A. Her deck, once red with heroes' blood
   B. Where knelt the vanquished foe
   C. The sun that brief December day
   D. The moon above the eastern wood

____ 12. Which of these lines most varies the regular iambic meter?
   A. Yet not to thine eternal resting place
   B. Should sink beneath the wave
   C. In the full strength of years, matron and maid
   D. We reached the barn with merry din

Vocabulary and Grammar

____ 13. Which word below could replace the italicized word in the phrase "*thoughtful* quietness"?
   A. pensive   C. ominous
   B. gloaming   D. querulous

____ 14. Which words best describe a respected father figure?
   A. ominous glowing   C. venerable patriarch
   B. querulous patriarch   D. venerable sepulcher

____ **15.** In which line below does a present participle modify a noun?

A. Ay, tear her tattered ensign down!

B. Yet not to thine eternal resting place

C. The lightning and the gale!

D. The snow had begun in the gloaming

Essay

16. Oliver Wendell Holmes helped convince the public to rally to save the ship called *Old Ironsides* from destruction. If Holmes had written an editorial instead of a poem, do you think it would have had the same effect on the public? Why or why not? Answer these questions in a brief essay. To support your opinion, cite specific examples from the poem, and consider the emotional responses that the examples produce.

17. Poets often use images from nature to provoke an emotional response. Describe how nature images in at least two of the poems provoke different emotions. Consider the emotions the speaker or narrator attempts to convey and the emotional response in the reader.

Vocabulary Warm-up Word Lists

Study these words from the selections. Then, complete the activities.

Word List A

adequately [AD uh kwuht lee] *adv.* sufficiently
   Zelda covered the topic <u>adequately</u> in her essay, and she received a grade of B+.

afforded [uh FORD uhd] *v.* gave; offered
   Our trip to Pennsylvania <u>afforded</u> us a chance to see the battlefield at Gettysburg.

assemblage [uh SEM bluhj] *n.* collection; cluster
   The officer delivered his pep talk to an <u>assemblage</u> of potential army recruits.

conspicuous [kuhn SPIK yoo uhs] *adj.* easy to see or notice; prominent
   In the parade, the grand marshal was <u>conspicuous</u> because of his dress uniform.

duplicated [DOOP luh kayt uhd] *v.* made a copy of
   That medallion was unique and could not be <u>duplicated.</u>

innumerable [i NOOM uhr uh buhl] *adj.* countless
   On a frosty, clear night, the stars in the sky seem <u>innumerable</u>.

merchandise [MERCH uhn dyz] *n.* goods; articles for purchase or sale
   At the flea market, there was a huge variety of <u>merchandise</u> on display.

portray [pohr TRAY] *v.* to depict or present; to describe
   Many biographers <u>portray</u> George Washington as courageous and heroic.

Word List B

deemed [DEEMD] *v.* considered as; thought to be
   Horse racing is often <u>deemed</u> the sport of kings.

façade [fuh SAD] *n.* the front of a building; an appearance
   The imposing <u>façade</u> of the building was at odds with the rather ordinary interior.

fraternal [fruh TERN uhl] *adj.* brotherly
   A <u>fraternal</u> relationship implies close ties and lasting bonds.

infinite [IN fuh nit] *adj.* without limit or restriction
   Otto's patience seems <u>infinite</u>, for nothing ever flusters him.

labyrinth [LAB i rinth] *n.* maze; intricate network
   Many companies have dealt with a <u>labyrinth</u> of complex laws.

mutually [MYOO choo uh lee] *adv.* jointly; in a way shared in common
   Yuri and Sasha were associated <u>mutually</u> in a tourist and hotel corporation.

prosecute [PRAH suh kyoot] *v.* to follow up or pursue to a conclusion
   We want to <u>prosecute</u> our marketing campaign to a successful conclusion.

resources [RE zohr suhz] *n.* available means of accomplishing something
   Due to limited <u>resources</u> in the town, the plan for a new park was not feasible.

Selections by Meriwether Lewis and John Wesley Powell
Vocabulary Warm-up Exercises

Exercise A *Fill in the blanks, using each word from Word List A only once.*

Sue was amazed by her first visit to a flea market. No department store

[1] _____ the experience of shopping at the hundreds of outdoor stalls, with

their [2] _____ of items clustered together and displayed for all to see.

[3] _____ signs drew her attention to huge discounts. There seemed to be no

way she could examine the [4] _____ quantities of [5] _____ :

antiques, second-hand furnishings, paintings, jewelry, and other knick-knacks. Her travels

had [6] _____ Sue the chance to shop in outdoor markets in many foreign

countries, yet the flea market outdid them all, and it was, relatively speaking, in her own

back yard, right here at home in the USA! She wondered how she could best

[7] _____ the color and bustling energy of the flea market. Perhaps the way

she could render the experience most [8] _____ was by painting the scene.

Exercise B *Revise each sentence so that the underlined vocabulary word is logical. Be sure to keep the vocabulary word in your revision.*

Example: Because the film was so <u>suspenseful</u>, we left before it ended.
Because the film was so <u>suspenseful</u>, we were on the edge of our seats.

1. Because she <u>deemed</u> that book a classic, the critic neglected to mention it.
   _____

2. We walked around to the rear in order to photograph the building's impressive <u>façade</u>.
   _____

3. We had an unstable, almost <u>fraternal</u> relationship with our neighbors.
   _____

4. A man of <u>infinite</u> patience, Sal flew off the handle at the slightest provocation.
   _____

5. It was no challenge at all to make our way through the twists and turns of the <u>labyrinth</u>.
   _____

6. The contract was <u>mutually</u> beneficial, with all the advantages going to management.
   _____

7. To <u>prosecute</u> a project to completion, it is unnecessary to have a step-by-step plan.
   _____

8. Because of its many <u>resources</u>, the foundation had trouble financing our study trip.
   _____

Selections by Meriwether Lewis and John Wesley Powell

Reading Warm-up A

Read the following passage. Pay special attention to the underlined words. Then, read it again, and complete the activities. Use a separate sheet of paper for your written answers.

In his essay, John Wesley Powell pays tribute to the wonders of the Grand Canyon. Powell admits, though, that it is nearly impossible to <u>portray</u> or describe this "sublime spectacle" in words.

One of Powell's companions on his excursions to the West, the painter Thomas Moran, also found it difficult to capture the immense vista of the Grand Canyon <u>adequately</u>. Moran first painted the Grand Canyon in 1872. When the United States government was <u>afforded</u> an opportunity to buy it, this picture became the first landscape by an American artist to be purchased by the government. The price of the <u>merchandise</u> was $10,000. Once purchased, the picture promptly went on display in the U.S. Capitol building. Here it joined an <u>assemblage</u> of busts, statues, and effigies—a collection of the likenesses of flesh-and-blood heroes.

For Thomas Moran, as for his painting's admirers, the real hero in the painting was the West itself—and its <u>innumerable</u>, seemingly inexhaustible natural splendors. The painting played a <u>conspicuous</u> role in encouraging wilderness tourism. It offered a thrilling view of one of nature's greatest spectacles. Moran, however, could not have believed that he had <u>duplicated</u> the real thing. Such a sight was simply too vast for any landscape painter to capture successfully. In the great vista of the Grand Canyon, there is no scale that allows the viewer to appreciate the sight in relation to the human body. As a result, when you look at Moran's painting you have trouble imagining yourself on the edge of the scene. Nevertheless, the artist continued for at least forty more years to experiment with ways to render the Grand Canyon.

1. Underline the words that give a clue to the meaning of <u>portray</u>. Use the word *portray* in an original sentence.

2. Circle the words that hint at the meaning of <u>adequately</u>. What is a synonym for *adequately*?

3. Underline the words that tell what was <u>afforded</u>. What is a synonym for *afforded*?

4. Circle the words in this and the next sentence that offer a clue to the meaning of <u>merchandise</u>.

5. Circle the words that offer clues to the meaning of <u>assemblage</u>. Give two synonyms for *assemblage*.

6. Underline the words that give a clue to the meaning of the word <u>innumerable</u>. What is a synonym for *innumerable*?

7. Circle the words in this and the next sentence that give a clue to the meaning of <u>conspicuous</u>. Use a word meaning the opposite of *conspicuous* in an original sentence.

8. Underline the words in this and the next sentence hinting at the meaning of <u>duplicated</u>. Use the word *duplicated* in an original sentence.

Name _____ Date _____

Read the following passage. Pay special attention to the underlined words. Then, read it again, and complete the activities. Use a separate sheet of paper for your written answers.

In the judgment of historians, a young Indian woman named Sacagawea has been <u>deemed</u> one of the most important contributors to the success of Lewis and Clark. Several months after the explorers departed from St. Louis to <u>prosecute</u> their historic exploration of the West, they arrived near what is now Bismarck, North Dakota, to spend the winter. Here they encountered Toussaint Charbonneau, a French Canadian trapper who had been living among the Mandan Indians and enjoyed <u>fraternal</u> relations with them. Lewis and Clark hired Charbonneau as an interpreter and guide.

Shortly before this meeting, Charbonneau had married a young Shoshone girl named Sacagawea, who had been a war captive captured by the Hidatsa Indians. In February 1805, Sacagawea have birth to a son. It was agreed that Sacagawea and her little boy would also accompany the expedition.

For Lewis and Clark, this decision was highly significant. Sacagawea turned out to be a more valuable guide than her husband. She identified plants, fruits, vegetables, and other food <u>resources</u> for the explorers. She displayed <u>infinite</u> amounts of courage, and her patience in the face of danger and hardship was said to have no limits. Perhaps most important, the presence of a woman and a small child with the expedition had a notable effect on the Indians whom the explorers encountered. For the Indians, Sacagawea and her little boy were no mere <u>façade</u> or meaningless front; they were, as Clark reported, "a token of peace." As an interpreter and guide, Sacagawea successfully guided the explorers through what might otherwise have been a confusing <u>labyrinth</u> of languages, customs, and cultures. She played a critical part in achieving peace agreements between the Indians and the white explorers, in which each party maintained a <u>mutually</u> respectful relationship.

1. Underline the words in this sentence that hint at the meaning of the word <u>deemed</u>. What is a synonym for *deemed*?

2. Circle the words in this sentence that hint at the meaning of <u>prosecute</u>. Use the word *prosecute* in an original sentence.

3. Underline the words in this sentence that hint at the meaning of <u>fraternal</u>. Use a word meaning the opposite of *fraternal* in an original sentence.

4. Underline the words in this sentence that hint at the meaning of <u>resources</u>. What are two synonyms for *resources*?

5. Circle the words in this sentence that hint at the meaning of <u>infinite</u>. What is an antonym for this word?

6. Circle the words in this sentence that give a good clue to the meaning of <u>façade</u>. Use this word in an original sentence.

7. Underline the words in this sentence that hint at the meaning of <u>labyrinth</u>. What is a synonym for *labyrinth*?

8. Underline the words in this sentence that hint at the meaning of <u>mutually</u>. What is a synonym for *mutually*?

"Crossing the Great Divide" by Meriwether Lewis
"The Most Sublime Spectacle on Earth" by John Wesley Powell
Literary Analysis: Description

Description is writing that captures sights, sounds, smells, tastes, and physical feelings or sensations. Through description, writers bring scenes and objects to life.

DIRECTIONS: *On the line after each passage, indicate whether the passage appeals to the sense of* sight, sound, taste, smell, *or* touch. *Some passages may appeal to more than one of the senses.*

1. We now formed our camp just below the junction of the forks on the Lard. [larboard] side in a level smooth bottom covered with a fine turf of greensward. Here we unloaded our canoes and arranged our baggage on shore; formed a canopy of one of our large sails and planted some willow brush in the ground to form a shade for the Indians to sit under while we spoke to them.

    _____

2. Consider a rock 200,000 square miles in extent and a mile in thickness, against which the clouds have hurled their storms and beat in into sands and the rills have carried the sands into the creeks and the creeks have carried them into the rivers and the Colorado has carried them into the sea.

    _____

3. The black gneiss below, the variegated quartzite, and the green or alcove sandstone form the foundation for the mighty red wall. The banded sandstone entablature is crowned by the tower limestone.

    _____

4. The river thunders in perpetual roar, swelling in floors of music when the storm gods play upon the rocks and fading away in soft and low murmurs when the infinite blue of heaven is unveiled.

    _____

5. Mountains of music swell in the rivers, hills of music billow in the creeks, and meadows of music murmur in the rills that ripple over the rocks. Altogether it is a symphony of multitudinous melodies. All this is the music of waters. The adamant foundations of the earth have been wrought into a sublime harp, upon which the clouds of the heavens play with mighty tempests or with gentle showers.

    _____

"Crossing the Great Divide" by Meriwether Lewis
"The Most Sublime Spectacle on Earth" by John Wesley Powell
Reading Strategy: Note Spatial Relationships

Keeping track of physical dimensions and relative positions of things—and comparing them with those of other objects—can help you envision what the writer is describing. Be alert for words and phrases that indicate spatial relationships, such as *behind, next to, in front of, at the bottom, on the left, in the north, inside, outside, above, below,* and *between.*

DIRECTIONS: *For each passage from the selections, underline the words or phrases that denote spatial relationships and answer the question or questions on the lines provided.*

1. Drewyer had been gone about 2 hours when an Indian who had straggled some little distance down the river returned and reported that the white men were coming, that he had seen them just below.

   In comparison with the speaker, where was the Indian when he saw the white men?

   _____

   Where were the white men?

   _____

2. The erosion represented in the canyons, although vast, is but a small part of the great erosion of the region, for between the cliffs blocks have been carried away far superior in magnitude to those necessary to fill the canyons.

   In relation to the cliffs, where were the blocks originally?

   _____

   Where are they now?

   _____

3. The black gneiss below, the variegated quartzite, and the green or alcove sandstone form the foundation for the mighty red wall. The banded sandstone entablature is crowned by the tower limestone.

   Where is the black gneiss relative to the other layers of rock?

   _____

   Where is the limestone relative to the other layers of rock?

   _____

"Crossing the Great Divide" by Meriwether Lewis
"The Most Sublime Spectacle on Earth" by John Wesley Powell
Vocabulary Builder

Using the Prefix *multi-*

A. DIRECTIONS: *The prefix* multi- *means "much" or "many." Use the prefix in the words you write to complete the following items.*

1. *Bi-* means "two." If a person who speaks two languages is *bilingual,* then a person who speaks many languages must be _____.

2. _____ wool is wool that combines many colors.

3. A one-dimensional character has only one personality trait, but a _____ character has quite a few personality traits.

4. *Uni-* means "one." If an amoeba is a *unicellular* creature, a human being must be a _____ creature.

5. If a military force has members from many nations, you might describe it as a _____ force.

Using the Word List

conspicuous	excavated	multifarious	sublime
demarcation	multitudinous	labyrinth	

B. DIRECTIONS: *On the lines provided, write a synonym for each italicized word.*

1. We took care to make them a *conspicuous* object of our own good wishes and the care of our government. _____

2. Yet all these canyons unite to form one grand canyon, the most *sublime* spectacle on the earth. _____

3. The vast *labyrinth* of canyon by which the plateau region drained by the Colorado is dissected is also the work of waters. _____

4. Every river has *excavated* its own gorge. _____

5. No plane of *demarcation* between wall and blue firmament can be seen. _____

6. The elements that unite to make the Grand Canyon the most sublime spectacle in nature are *multifarious.* _____

7. The forms are wrought into endless details, to describe which would be a task equal in magnitude to that of describing the stars of the heavens or the *multitudinous* beauties of the forest. _____

_____

Name _____ Date _____

"Crossing the Great Divide" by Meriwether Lewis
"The Most Sublime Spectacle on Earth" by John Wesley Powell
Grammar and Style: Participial Phrases

A **participial phrase** consists of a present or past participle and its modifiers and complements. The entire phrase serves as an adjective, modifying a noun or pronoun. In the first sentence below, for example, the participial phrase consists of a present participle, *carrying*, plus its complement, the direct object *sand*. The entire participial phrase works as an adjective, modifying the noun *creeks*. In the second sentence below, the participial phrase *drained by the Colorado* consists of a past participle, *drained*, plus a modifier, the prepositional phrase *by the Colorado*. The entire participial phrase modifies the noun *region*.

Carrying sand, the many creeks join the Colorado River.

The plateau region *drained by the Colorado* is dissected by canyons.

A. PRACTICE: *Underline the participial phrases in the following sentences, and circle the nouns or pronouns that they modify.*

1. Each is a composite structure, a wall composed of many walls.

2. The erosion represented in the canyons, although vast, is but a small part of the great erosion of the region.

3. The heavens mount into a vast dome spanning the Grand Canyon with empyrean blue.

B. Writing Application: *For each item below, write a sentence with a participial phrase that modifies the noun provided.*

1. river _____

_____

2. canoes _____

_____

3. canyon _____

_____

4. gorge _____

_____

Name _____ Date _____

Support for Writing

After you choose a natural wonder, prepare to write a description based on something you have seen, researched on the Internet, or learned from a film. Use the chart below to organize your ideas or make a chart of your own.

Name of Natural Wonder		
Feature 1	description/colors, shapes, spatial words	feelings about feature
Feature 2	description/colors, shapes, spatial words	feelings about feature
Feature 3	description/colors, shapes, spatial words	feelings about feature
Feature 4	description/colors, shapes, spatial words	feelings about feature

On a separate page, write a draft of your description of the natural wonder. As you revise, add important details or take out less important ones. Be sure your revision includes a description of how the natural wonder makes you feel.

Name _____ Date _____

"Crossing the Great Divide" by Meriwether Lewis
"The Most Sublime Spectacle on Earth" by John Wesley Powell
Support for Extend Your Learning

Listening and Speaking

As you work with a small group to prepare a **tourism presentation** of a trip by raft down the Colorado River through the Grand Canyon, focus on these aspects:

- Present a vivid description of the sights by using lively adjectives.
- Provide an explanation of what rafting through the Grand Canyon will be like.
- Offer a list of clothing and equipment to take along.

Find slides or download photos of the Grand Canyon from the Internet to add to your presentation.

Research and Technology

As you prepare an **expedition map** of the Lewis and Clark journey from St. Louis to the Oregon Coast, enter information from the Internet on the note-taking list below. Use a second sheet of paper, and a map of the United States as a guide, to draw a rough map of the expedition before you use the desktop format.

Map of Lewis and Clark Expedition
Start and Finish Points
Miles Traveled
Rivers Traveled and Mountains Crossed
Important Places Seen
Animals and Plants Discovered
Native Americans Met

When you make your desktop map, you might enter some of the natural flora and fauna of the West that the two explorers found and where they found each species.

Unit 3 Resources: A Growing Nation

Name _____ Date _____

Enrichment: Social Studies

DIRECTIONS: *In your social studies textbook or in a library reference book, find a map of the United States at the time of the Louisiana Purchase. Use this map to answer the following questions about the territory of the Louisiana Purchase.*

1. Which territory was on the northeastern border of the Louisiana Purchase?

   _____

2. Describe how the Louisiana Purchase changed the border of the western United States.

   _____

   _____

   _____

3. To which large body of water did the United States gain direct passage with the Louisiana Purchase?

   _____

4. About how many miles did Lewis and Clark travel more than they would have if they had traveled in a straight line from St. Louis to the Pacific coast and back to St. Louis?

   _____

   _____

   _____

5. How many states were part of the United States at the time of the Louisiana Purchase? List them.

   _____

   _____

   _____

   _____

   _____

6. When Lewis and Clark explored the territory gained with the Louisiana Purchase, they claimed Oregon Country for the United States. Knowing this, explain why the acquisition of the Louisiana Purchase began a century-long era of westward expansion.

   _____

   _____

   _____

   _____

   _____

   _____

Name _____ Date _____

"Crossing the Great Divide" by Meriwether Lewis
"The Most Sublime Spectacle on Earth" by John Wesley Powell
Selection Test A

Critical Reading *Identify the letter of the choice that best answers the question.*

____ 1. In "Crossing the Great Divide," what is Lewis's main goal?

A. to get help from Native Americans

B. to save food for the trip

C. to get horses for land travel

D. to find canoes for water travel

____ 2. What kind of writing is shown in this passage from "Crossing the Great Divide"?

Here we unloaded our canoes and arranged our baggage on shore; formed a canopy of one of our large sails and planted some willow brush in the ground to form a shade for the Indians to sit under . . .

A. fiction writing

B. descriptive writing

C. persuasive writing

D. instruction writing

____ 3. Why did Lewis and Clark ask Labuish, Charbono, and Sah-ca-ga-we-ah to help them communicate with other Native Americans in "Crossing the Great Divide"?

A. Lewis and Clark did not get along with them.

B. They could understand both English and Native American languages.

C. The three people could speak on behalf of their tribes.

D. Lewis and Clark did not have anything to offer the Native Americans.

____ 4. What element of the Grand Canyon is described in this passage from "The Most Sublime Spectacle on Earth"?

The Grand Canyon of the Colorado is a canyon composed of many canyons. It is a composite of thousands, of tens of thousands, of gorges.

A. its shape

B. its color

C. its location

D. its size

____ 5. In "The Most Sublime Spectacle on Earth," how does Powell convey the depth of the canyon?

A. by saying that dropping tall mountains into the canyon would not fill it up

B. by saying that the clouds and their weather have formed the canyon

C. by explaining that the canyon region gets very little rain in any given year

D. by describing the colors of the different rock layers seen in the canyon

6. On which feature of the Grand Canyon's walls does Powell focus in "The Most Sublime Spectacle on Earth"?
    A. their smoothness
    B. their colors
    C. their erosion
    D. their age

7. In "The Most Sublime Spectacle on Earth," Powell says that describing the Grand Canyon is as hard as describing the beauties of the forest. How does this passage lead you to picture the forest?

    with its . . . oak and pine and poplar . . . tulip and lily and rose . . .fern and moss . . .

    A. from side to side
    B. from bottom to top
    C. from far away to close up
    D. from top to bottom

8. According to this passage from "The Most Sublime Spectacle on Earth," what causes the "music" heard in the Grand Canyon?

    Mountains of music swell in the rivers, hills of music billow in the creeks, and meadows of music murmur in the rills that ripple over the rocks.

    A. mountains
    B. meadows
    C. water
    D. singing people

Vocabulary and Grammar

9. In which of the following phrases is the meaning of the word *excavated* expressed?
    A. "The glories and the beauties of form, color, and sound unite . . ."
    B. "cannot be adequately represented in symbols of speech . . ."
    C. "blocks are upheaved from beneath the sea by internal geologic forces . . ."
    D. "the clouds play in the canyon, as they often do in the rainy season . . ."

10. Which of the following contains a participial phrase?
    A. ". . . the work of rains and rivers . . ."
    B. ". . . the clouds belong to the sky . . ."
    C. ". . . a wall composed of many walls . . ."
    D. ". . . the Grand Canyon in one view . . ."

Essay

11. In "Crossing the Great Divide," what kinds of things did Lewis say to the Native Americans he met about how they would be treated by the U.S. government? Were these things true or not? Why do you think he said these things? Write a brief essay to explain your opinion. Use at least two examples from "Crossing the Great Divide" to support your opinion.

12. In "The Most Sublime Spectacle on Earth," John Wesley Powell describes the Grand Canyon as a "land of song." Which of the five senses—taste, touch, sound, sight, and smell—is he using to describe the canyon? How might this description have helped people who had never seen the canyon understand it? Write a brief essay explaining how Powell's description helped readers get a better sense of what the Grand Canyon was like.

"Crossing the Great Divide" by Meriwether Lewis
"The Most Sublime Spectacle on Earth" by John Wesley Powell
Selection Test B

Critical Reading *Identify the letter of the choice that best completes the statement or answers the question.*

_____ 1. The selection from Lewis's journal focuses on
   A. the reasons Lewis and Clark are making their journey across the continent.
   B. the danger, beauty, and excitement of crossing the Great Divide.
   C. the excitement of viewing the Grand Canyon for the first time.
   D. Clark's return with Charbono and the expedition's relations with local tribes.

_____ 2. Lewis most likely sent Shields to hunt because
   A. food had to be replenished since it could not be easily preserved on the journey.
   B. the expedition needed a certain type of food to offer its Native American guests.
   C. Shields had nothing to do, and Lewis wanted to keep him busy.
   D. Lewis himself was unskilled at hunting.

_____ 3. From where was the expedition obtaining the horses described in the selection?
   A. from Captain Clark's party
   B. from President Thomas Jefferson
   C. from Shields, who hunted down the wild mustangs and rounded them up for the expedition
   D. from the Indians

_____ 4. "We now formed our camp just below the junction of the forks on the Lard, side in a level smooth bottom covered with a fine turf of greensward" is an example of
   A. persuasive writing.
   B. fictional writing.
   C. descriptive writing.
   D. biographical writing.

_____ 5. According to the remark, "We now formed our camp just below the junction of the forks," the camp is probably
   A. upstream, before the junction.
   B. downstream, after the junction.
   C. at the top of a cliff, beside the junction.
   D. underground, beneath the junction.

_____ 6. Lewis and Clark met with the Indians near the river in order to _____.
   A. talk
   B. trade
   C. fish
   D. fight

____ 7. Based on the details in Lewis's journals, you can conclude that the preferred method of travel for the Lewis and Clark expedition was
   A. on horseback.
   B. by water.
   C. in a wagon train.
   D. on foot.

____ 8. What chief emotion does the Grand Canyon inspire in Powell?
   A. fear
   B. envy
   C. optimism
   D. awe

____ 9. Based on the details in "The Most Sublime Spectacle on Earth," the erosion in the Grand Canyon seems to be caused primarily by _____.
   A. water
   B. wind
   C. ice
   D. heat

____ 10. According to Powell's descriptions, what is the most striking visual feature of the Grand Canyon's walls?
   A. texture
   B. color
   C. erosion
   D. age

____ 11. Powell writes:
   Pluck up Mt. Washington by the roots to the level of the sea and drop it headfirst into the Grand Canyon, and the dam will not force its waters over the walls. Pluck up the Blue Ridge and hurl it into the Grand Canyon, and it will not fill it.

   How does this passage help the reader appreciate the Grand Canyon?
   A. It helps the reader picture the location of the Grand Canyon.
   B. It helps the reader picture the colors of the Grand Canyon.
   C. It helps the reader picture the size of the Grand Canyon.
   D. It helps the reader picture how Powell cleared a path for future explorers.

____ 12. Powell describes the walls of the Grand Canyon as follows:
   The black gneiss below, the variegated quartzite, and the green or alcove sandstone form the foundation for the mighty red wall. The banded sandstone entablature is crowned by the tower limestone.

   This description leads you to visualize the wall from
   A. left to right.
   B. near to far.
   C. top to bottom.
   D. bottom to top.

____ 13. What are the sources of most of the "music" that Powell describes in "The Most Sub-lime Spectacle on Earth"?
  A. animals and falling rocks
  B. clouds and wind
  C. rivers and creeks
  D. campers singing

____ 14. Which passage best illustrates descriptive writing?
  A. "This morning I arose very early and dispatched Drewyer and the Indian down the river."
  B. "The heavens constitute a portion of the facade and mount into a vast dome from wall to wall, spanning the Grand Canyon with empyrean blue."
  C. "The wonders of the Grand Canyon cannot be adequately represented in symbols of speech, nor by speech itself."
  D. "It is a region more difficult to traverse than the Alps or the Himalayas."

Vocabulary and Grammar

____ 15. Which statement is most likely true about a *labyrinth*?
  A. It is easy to pass through, with no lines or planes of demarcation.
  B. The exit is conspicuous.
  C. Finding your way through it can be sublime and exhilarating.
  D. It is one smooth surface that has never been excavated.

____ 16. What noun does the participial phrase in this sentence modify?
  The Grand Canyon of the Colorado is a canyon composed of many canyons.

  A. Grand Canyon
  B. Colorado
  C. canyon
  D. canyons

Essay

17. In addition to exploring the territory gained in the Louisiana Purchase, Lewis and Clark were to establish friendly relations with the Native Americans they met along the way. Briefly explain why this was important. Include at least two reasons presented in the selection.

18. As Powell, Lewis, and Clark explored new territories, they encountered many adventures as well as discomforts and dangers. Do you think Powell or Lewis would look forward to another journey? Write an essay describing some of the positive and negative experiences the explorers encountered. Use examples from the text to predict whether or not they would choose to make another exploration under similar conditions.

19. John Wesley Powell was a trained geologist, at one point a geology professor at a university. A geologist is a scientist who studies the earth's surface and a variety of things and actions upon it, including soils, rocks, caves, bodies of water, and erosion of the earth's surface. Write an essay explaining how geology seems to have influenced Powell's writing. Use details from the selection to support your evaluation.

Vocabulary Warm-up Word Lists

Study these words from the selections. Then, complete the activities.

Word List A

alternately [AWL tuhr nuht lee] *adv.* in succession; taking turns
Tom was <u>alternately</u> hopeful and pessimistic, and could not make up his mind.

boon [BOON] *n.* welcome benefit; favor
The high grade on his math exam was a <u>boon</u> to James, giving him encouragement.

enchantment [en CHANT muhnt] *n.* state of being charmed; magical spell
During the concert, the flute solo was a delightful source of <u>enchantment</u>.

ghastly [GAST lee] *adj.* horrible; frightful
The television pictures of the war casualties were <u>ghastly</u>.

maturity [muh CHOOR uh tee] *n.* state or quality of being full-grown
In <u>maturity</u>, a full-grown male Bengal tiger weighs about 450 pounds.

similarly [SIM uh luhr lee] *adv.* likewise
Homer's *Iliad* is an epic poem; <u>similarly</u>, *Beowulf* is also an epic focusing on a hero.

sinister [SIN is tuhr] *adj.* threatening harm or evil
We could tell that the villain in that TV show had <u>sinister</u> intentions.

somber [SOM buhr] *adj.* dark and gloomy; depressed
The solemn music at the funeral put everyone in a <u>somber</u> mood.

Word List B

acuteness [uh KYOOT nis] *n.* sharpness; keenness
The <u>acuteness</u> of most dogs' hearing surpasses human abilities.

apathy [AP uh thee] *n.* lack of interest or feeling; indifference
The class listened with <u>apathy</u> to the speaker.

demeanor [duh MEEN uhr] *n.* outward behavior or conduct
Sarah was known for her shy <u>demeanor</u>.

gradual [GRAD yoo uhl] *adj.* taking place by slow steps or degrees
Progress on that issue will have to be <u>gradual</u> and can't be achieved overnight.

inaccessible [in ak SES uh buhl] *adj.* impossible to reach or enter
Their house is <u>inaccessible</u> except by helicopter.

sensibility [sen si BIL uh tee] *n.* capacity for being affected emotionally
Pete was respected for his <u>sensibility</u> to other people's problems.

solace [SAHL uhs] *n.* comfort; consolation
The old man found <u>solace</u> in the visit of his grandchildren.

succumbed [suh KUMD] *v.* yielded to; gave way; submitted to
Debbie <u>succumbed</u> to temptation and ordered a chocolate ice cream soda.

Name _____ Date _____

Vocabulary Warm-up Exercises

Exercise A *Fill in the blanks, using each word from Word List A only once.*

Tim's new hobby was recording the musical scores of action thrillers. Movies fascinated him, and he felt that when he reached [1] _____ as an adult, his career would somehow be connected with film. Tim [2] _____ considered acting, directing, and composing; he was [3] _____ talented at all three. It was the combination of music and visual images, though, that held the most [4] _____ for him. He appreciated the ways a gifted composer could use music to express a(n) [5] _____ mood of disappointment, or foreshadow an ominous or [6] _____ plot development. Music could create optimism, Tim thought, when the hero or heroine was overjoyed by a(n) [7] _____; music could also drive home the [8] _____ aspects of a horrible catastrophe. Tim thought that before the end of the year, he would try to write his own musical score for a full-length feature film.

Exercise B *Decide whether each statement below is true or false. Circle T or F, and explain your answer.*

1. When someone answers a question with *acuteness*, you can trust the answer as reliable.
   T / F _____

2. *Apathy* usually indicates a person's kindness and concern.
   T / F _____

3. A person's *demeanor* refers to his or her inner emotional state.
   T / F _____

4. A *gradual* series of events often unfolds over a considerable span of time.
   T / F _____

5. An office that is *inaccessible* is easy to find and is open to everyone.
   T / F _____

6. A person whose *sensibility* is fine-tuned does not usually consider others' feelings.
   T / F _____

7. If you find *solace* in a time of grief, your sorrows are increased.
   T / F _____

8. People who have *succumbed* to invaders have mounted a successful challenge to them.
   T / F _____

Name _____ Date _____

Selections by Edgar Allan Poe
Reading Warm-up A

Read the following passage. Pay special attention to the underlined words. Then, read it again, and complete the activities. Use a separate sheet of paper for your written answers.

In Edgar Allan Poe's poem, the raven is a gloomy, somber bird whose appearance first surprises but then deeply unsettles the speaker. At the start, the raven seems like a boon: a special sign of favor. As the poem progresses, however, the speaker loses all sense of fascination or enchantment. Instead, the raven becomes a ghastly, terrifying reminder of personal tragedy.

In real life, ravens are fascinating, highly intelligent birds that have inspired much study and admiration by humans. The Common Raven (*Corvus corax*) is the largest perching bird in the world. At maturity, adult birds have a length of over two feet and a wingspan of four feet. Ravens are sometimes mistaken for crows. The two species are similarly sooty-colored, but ravens have a much heavier beak and shaggier plumage than crows do.

Although they have often been held to symbolize death and disease, ravens are extremely intelligent and courageous birds. They have inspired many tales, especially among the native peoples of the Northwest Pacific Coast. For Native American storytellers, Raven was a bird-human character who was alternately clever and stupid by turns. He could be a grim and sinister figure, spreading confusion with his irresponsible tricks and greedy appetite. On the other hand, he was also a culture hero, who discovered light to transform the dark earth into a fruitful physical environment. Native American mythology and symbolism of Raven reflect the fascinating contrasts and opposites of this species of bird in real life.

1. Underline the words in this sentence that give a clue to the meaning of underlined somber. Use the word *somber* in an original sentence.

2. Circle the words in this sentence that give a clue to the meaning of boon. Would a *boon* normally be an advantage or a drawback?

3. Underline the words that hint at the meaning of enchantment here. Does this word have positive or negative associations?

4. Underline the words in this sentence that give a clue to the meaning of ghastly. What are two synonyms for *ghastly*?

5. Circle the words in this sentence that hint at the meaning of maturity. What is an antonym for *maturity*?

6. Circle the words in this sentence that offer a clue to the meaning of the word similarly. What is a synonym for *similarly*?

7. What is a synonym for alternately? Use the word *alternately* in a sentence of your own.

8. Underline the words that give a clue to the meaning of sinister. What are two synonyms for *sinister*?

Selections by Edgar Allan Poe
Reading Warm-up B

Read the following passage. Pay special attention to the underlined words. Then, read it again, and complete the activities. Use a separate sheet of paper for your written answers.

In May 1842, Edgar Allan Poe published a magazine review of Nathaniel Hawthorne's first short story collection, *Twice-Told Tales*. The review continues to be read because it concisely presents Poe's theory of the short story, a form that he called the "prose tale."

Poe believed that stories were superior to novels. In a story, which can be read at one sitting, a writer can present a single total effect. The acuteness with which a reader keenly experiences this effect cannot be duplicated in a novel. The reading of a novel, Poe pointed out, is gradual, with many interruptions from start to finish. The reader's sensibility for the characters and situation is often distracted. Poe thought that the end result might be apathy, or actual indifference to the characters and the storyline. In any event, the length of novels ruled out the impact of a single effect, making such an effect inaccessible to the reader. By contrast, in beginning to read a short story, the reader has succumbed to the writer's control, yielding all of his or her attention from the beginning to the end.

To reinforce his main idea, Poe argued that every detail in a short story should contribute to the writer's single effect. Poe even specified that a story's single effect should be clear in the tale's very first sentence. To test Poe's theory, read the first sentence of "The Fall of the House of Usher" several times. In this long first sentence, you will find at least ten words and phrases with melancholy, even ominous connotations or associations. The narrator's outward demeanor is heavy-hearted and depressed, and he sees no comfort or solace in his horseback ride on a gloomy autumn afternoon. In his first sentence, Poe brilliantly establishes the prevailing mood or atmosphere of the tale to come.

1. Underline the words in this sentence that give a clue to the meaning of underline{acuteness}. Use the word **acuteness** in an original sentence.

2. Circle the word in this sentence that gives a clue to the meaning of underline{gradual}. Use a word meaning the opposite of **gradual** in a sentence of your own.

3. Underline the words in this sentence hinting at the meaning of underline{sensibility}.

4. Underline the words in this sentence that give a clue to the meaning of underline{apathy}. What are two antonyms for **apathy**?

5. Circle the words in this sentence that give a clue to the meaning of the word underline{inaccessible}. Use a word meaning the opposite of **inaccessible** in a sentence of your own.

6. Underline the words in this sentence that hint at the meaning of underline{succumbed}. What is an antonym of **succumbed**?

7. Underline the word in this sentence that gives a clue to the meaning of underline{demeanor}.

8. Circle the words in this sentence that hint at the meaning of the word underline{solace}. What is a synonym for **solace**?

"The Fall of the House of Usher" and "The Raven" by Edgar Allan Poe
Literary Analysis: Single Effect

Edgar Allan Poe said that a short story should be written to create a **single effect.** Every character, detail, and incident, from the first sentence on, should contribute to this effect. Certainly the effect of "The Fall of the House of Usher" is one of eerie terror, with mounting dread in every scene.

DIRECTIONS: *Following are settings and characters described in "The Fall of the House of Usher." On the lines below each setting or character, list three specific details about that setting or character that you feel contribute to the single effect.*

1. *Setting:* The room in which Usher spends his days

   A. _____

   B. _____

   C. _____

2. *Setting:* Madeline's tomb

   A. _____

   B. _____

   C. _____

3. *Setting:* The house at the end of the story

   A. _____

   B. _____

   C. _____

4. *Character:* Roderick Usher

   A. _____

   B. _____

   C. _____

5. *Character:* Madeline Usher

   A. _____

   B. _____

   C. _____

Name _____ Date _____

Reading Strategy: Break Down Long Sentences

When an author writes a long, complicated sentence, you can clarify the meaning by breaking it down into its logical parts. Look especially for the subject and predicate at its core. After you have identified them, state the core in your own words.

Poe's sentence:	A cadaverousness of complexion; an eye large, liquid, and luminous beyond comparison; lips somewhat thin and very pallid, but of a surpassingly beautiful curve; a nose of a delicate Hebrew model, but with a breath of nostril unusual in similar formations; a finely molded chin, speaking, in its want of prominence, of a want of moral energy; hair of a more than weblike softness and tenuity— these features, with an inordinate expansion above the region of the temple, made up altogether a countenance not easily to be forgotten.
Core sentence:	These features made up a countenance not easily forgotten.
Own words:	He had a memorable face.

DIRECTIONS: *Underline the core of the following sentences from "The Fall of the House of Usher." Then restate the core in your own words.*

1. During the whole of a dull, dark, and soundless day in the autumn of that year, when the clouds hung oppressively low in the heavens, I had been passing alone, on horseback, through a singularly dreary tract of country, and at length found myself, as the shades of evening drew on, within view of the melancholy House of Usher.

   _____

2. I reined my horse to the precipitous brink of a black and lurid tarn that lay in unruffled luster by the dwelling, and gazed down—but with a shudder even more thrilling than before—upon the remodeled and inverted images of the gray sedge, and the ghastly tree stems, and the vacant and eyelike windows.

   _____

3. He admitted, however, although with hesitation, that much of the peculiar gloom which thus afflicted him could be traced to a more natural and far more palpable origin—to the severe and long-continued illness—indeed to the evidently approaching dissolution of a tenderly beloved sister, his sole companion for long years, his last and only relative on earth.

   _____

4. Our books—the books which, for years, had formed no small portion of the mental existence of the invalid—were, as might be supposed, in strict keeping with this character of phantasm.

   _____

"The Fall of the House of Usher" and "The Raven" by Edgar Allan Poe
Vocabulary Builder

Using the Root -voc-

A. DIRECTIONS: *The root -voc- comes from the Latin* vox, *meaning "voice." On the lines provided, explain how the root -voc- influences the meaning of each of the italicized words.*

1. The environmental board in our town *advocates* passage of a strong law against dumping waste in Lake Jasper.

   _____

2. Studying the works of Poe will probably improve your *vocabulary*.

   _____

3. The cottage was *evocative* of happy childhood memories.

   _____

Using the Word List

importunate	appellation	sentience	munificent	specious
obeisance	equivocal	anomalous	craven	

B. DIRECTIONS: *For each item, write on the line the letter of the pair of words that expresses a relationship most like the pair in capital letters.*

____ 1. JESSICA : APPELLATION ::
    A. light : sun   B. magenta : color   C. government : nation

____ 2. FALSE : SPECIOUS ::
    A. beautiful : ugly   B. violent : wicked   C. plentiful : abundant

____ 3. NORMAL : ANOMALOUS ::
    A. valuable : worthless   B. blue : color   C. sleepy : tired

____ 4. EQUIVOCAL : SURE ::
    A. physician : disease   B. vocal : talkative   C. vague : clear

____ 5. SENTIENCE : FEELING ::
    A. capable: skill   B. visible : darkness   C. worth : value

____ 6. BENEFACTOR : MUNIFICENT ::
    A. donor : charity   B. giver : taker   C. philanthropist : generous

____ 7. IMPORTUNATE : INSIST ::
    A. unlucky : luck   B. talkative : chat   C. create : thought

____ 8. HERO : CRAVEN ::
    A. villain : evil   B. raven : black   C. diplomat : tactless

____ 9. BOW : OBEISANCE ::
    A. salute : hand   B. smile : happiness   C. frown : joy

Name _____ Date _____

"The Fall of the House of Usher" and **"The Raven"** by Edgar Allan Poe

Grammar and Style: Coordinate Adjectives

Coordinate adjectives are adjectives of equal rank that separately modify a noun. They should be separated by commas or coordinating conjunctions (such as *and* or *or*).

> that *abrupt, weighty, unhurried, and hollow-sounding* enunciation
> a *pestilent and mystic* vapor

Adjectives that do not separately modify their noun are not coordinate and do not need commas or a conjunction between them. In the following example, *certain* and *boyish* do not separately modify the noun *traits*; instead, *certain* modifies the entire phrase *boyish traits*.

> reminiscences of *certain boyish traits*

Usually, if the order of the adjectives can be reversed with no change in meaning, they are coordinate.

A. PRACTICE: *On the line before each phrase below, label the adjectives C for coordinate or NC for not coordinate. Add commas in the phrases where necessary.*

_____ 1. a black and lurid tarn

_____ 2. acute bodily illness

_____ 3. an eye large liquid and luminous

_____ 4. his peculiar physical conformation

_____ 5. stern deep and irredeemable gloom

B. Writing Application: *On the lines provided, write a phrase that describes each noun with two or more coordinate adjectives, and then another phrase that describes it with two or more adjectives that are not coordinate. Be sure to punctuate your phrases correctly.*

1. coordinate: _____ raven

   not coordinate: _____ raven

2. coordinate: _____ tarn

   not coordinate: _____ tarn

3. coordinate: _____ mansion

   not coordinate: _____ mansion

4. coordinate: _____ friend

   not coordinate: _____ friend

"The Fall of the House of Usher" and **"The Raven"** by Edgar Allan Poe
Support for Writing

As you prepare to write a **critical essay** of "The Fall of the House of Usher," first reread the story and decide which of the following views you support:

- The narrator of the story is insane.
- Each character represents one of the following: the conscious mind, the unconscious mind, the soul.
- The house itself is connected to the inhabitants and cannot continue standing after they are dead.

Now enter details from your rereading in the chart below.

Critical Appraisal of "The Fall of the House of Usher"	
Main Idea about What is Going on in Story	Expansion of Main Idea
Support from first part of story	
Support from middle of story	
Support from end of story	

On a separate page, write a draft of your critical essay. When you revise your work, be sure that your point of view is stated clearly and that the examples you give from the story support this point of view.

"The Fall of the House of Usher" and **"The Raven"** by Edgar Allan Poe

Support for Extend Your Learning

Listening and Speaking

As you prepare to give a **dramatic reading** of "The Raven," reread it to yourself. Then follow these tips to help capture the poem's tension and bring its rhythms and rhymes to life:

- Record yourself on audio- or videotape.
- Review your presentation for possible lack of clarity or dramatic effect.
- Use body language to help convey the poem's meaning.

In your performance, be sure to speak clearly. Use your voice dramatically to convey the rising emotion of the speaker.

Research and Technology

To prepare for a **class discussion** on how writers and filmmakers create suspense, watch an Alfred Hitchcock film with a group. Compare the ways in which Hitchcock and Poe create suspense and fear. Enter information about how the film and "The Raven" create suspense differently from one another in the side sections of the diagram below. Enter information about how the film and "The Raven" create suspense in a similar way in the middle part of the diagram.

Fear and Suspense in Movies and Books

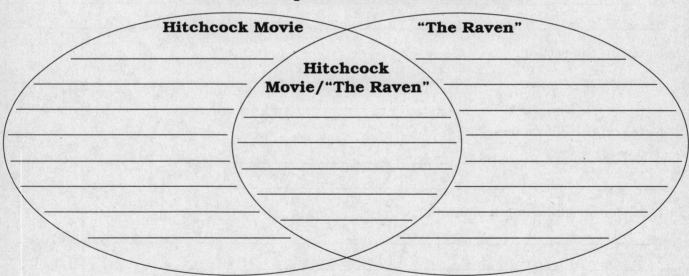

Now, have a class discussion about the two ways of creating mystery and suspense. Take a vote to see which way your group thinks is more effective in creating a sense of fear in the audience.

Name _____ Date _____

"The Fall of the House of Usher" and "The Raven" by Edgar Allan Poe
Enrichment: Film Versions of Edgar Allan Poe Stories

Because of their vividly imagined and terrifying worlds, Poe's short stories have often been adapted for film. Film versions of stories such as "The Fall of the House of Usher" (1982), "The Pit and the Pendulum" (1961), "The Tell-Tale Heart" (1963), "The Premature Burial" (1962), and "The Murders in the Rue Morgue" (1971) exist in video form today. Others appear from time to time on television.

DIRECTIONS: *Choose a scene from "The Fall of the House of Usher" or "The Raven" that you think would be especially suitable for a film or video interpretation. Recalling horror stories you have seen on television or at the movies, consider how you might film your scene. Focus on creating the right mood and effect. You may want to begin by looking at some suspense and horror videos of Poe's work. Note the techniques used to create mood and effect. Think about how you will handle the narration in Poe's stories. What will the setting be like? How will the characters look, dress, and move? Write a script for your scene that includes not only lines, but also descriptions of the setting, the characters and their actions, camera shots, and special visual and sound effects.*

Plan your scene in the following space.

Chosen scene:

_____

_____

Notes on the setting:

_____

_____

Notes on the characters:

_____

_____

Ideas for special camera shots:

_____

_____

Ideas for visual and sound effects:

_____

_____

"The Fall of the House of Usher" and "The Raven" by Edgar Allan Poe
Selection Test A

Critical Reading *Identify the letter of the choice that best answers the question.*

_____ 1. In "The Fall of the House of Usher," which word best describes the single effect created by the opening description of the house?
A. interest
B. gloom
C. enthusiasm
D. sorrow

_____ 2. Which choice below best restates this long sentence from "The Fall of the House of Usher"?

> Feeble beams of encrimsoned light made their way through the trellised panes, and served to render sufficiently distinct the more prominent objects around; the eye, however, struggled in vain to reach the remoter angles of the chamber or the recesses of the vaulted and fretted ceiling.

A. Not enough light came through the windowpanes, and I had trouble seeing even the larger objects in the room.
B. The light that came through the windows was so dim that it made everything in the room seem shadowy.
C. The dim light coming through the windows lit up the larger objects, but my eye could not see anything in the corners of the room.
D. The reddish light coming through the windows helped my eyes focus on everything in the room.

_____ 3. In "The Fall of the House of Usher," what does the narrator find to be the explanation for his host's sad situation?
A. the condition of the old house
B. the unending gloomy weather
C. his sister's mortal illness
D. his own failing health

_____ 4. Which passage best represents the single effect of "The Fall of the House of Usher?"
A. ". . . I scanned more narrowly the real aspect of the building."
B. ". . . with the first glimpse of the building, a sense of insufferable gloom pervaded my spirit."
C. ". . . there grew in my mind a strange fancy—a fancy so ridiculous . . ."
D. ". . . a light step on an adjoining staircase arrested my attention."

_____ **5.** Which choice below best restates this long sentence from "The Fall of the House of Usher"?

> Oppressed, as I certainly was, upon the extraordinary coincidence, by a thousand conflicting sensations, in which wonder and extreme terror were predominant, I still retained sufficient presence of mind to avoid exciting, by an observation, the sensitive nervousness of my companion.

A. Though I was oppressed by many feelings, the feeling of terror and nervousness were the two strongest.

B. I was overcome by many difficult emotions and was unable to avoid upsetting my friend.

C. I felt many different responses, but realized that my friend, had not observed it at all.

D. Though the coincidence overcame me with many feelings, including terror, I was careful to avoid upsetting my friend.

_____ **6.** In "The Raven," which of these elements contributes to the poem's single effect?
  I.   the repetition of words
  II. the meter
  III. the five-line stanzas
  IV. the poet's sorrow
A. I, II, III
B. I, III, IV
C. II, III, IV
D. I, II, IV

_____ **7.** When the poet in "The Raven" thinks that Lenore may be at his door, what are his feelings?
A. fear and anguish
B. hope and doubt
C. anger and disgust
D. curiosity and relief

_____ **8.** Which of these identifies a main cause and effect relationship in "The Raven"?
A. poetry and happiness
B. loss and heartbreak
C. sleeplessness and illness
D. strange visitors and dreams

Vocabulary and Grammar

____ 9. In which of these sentences is the meaning of the word *sentience* expressed?

A. The rocky crag stood in eternal silence over the town.

B. The forest floor rustled with scurrying forms of life.

C. The deep well reflected the old house in its waters.

D. The portraits in the dark room were barely visible.

____ 10. Which of the phrases below uses coordinate adjectives?

A. "As of someone gently rapping, rapping . . ."

B. "In there stepped a stately Raven . . ."

C. "Much I marveled this ungainly fowl . . ."

D. "And the silken, sad, uncertain rustling . . ."

Essay

11. In what ways are Roderick and Madeline Usher, and the house in which they live, alike? Are they healthy and lively, or dying and decaying? Why have they fallen into the state of health they are in? Write a brief essay to compare the siblings and the house from "The Fall of the House of Usher."

12. Many writers often use birds as symbols of hope, freedom, and light. In what different way does Poe use the image of the raven in his poem, "The Raven"? Write a brief essay to give your opinion about what the raven symbolizes in Poe's poem. Use at least two examples from the poem to support your opinion.

"The Fall of the House of Usher" and **"The Raven"** by Edgar Allan Poe

Selection Test B

Critical Reading *Identify the letter of the choice that best completes the statement or answers the question.*

_____ 1. Which of these words best describes the single effect created by the opening description of the house in "The Fall of the House of Usher"?
- A. sadness
- B. terror
- C. wariness
- D. curiosity

_____ 2. The letter that the narrator receives hints that Roderick Usher will be
- A. dull and depressed.
- B. suspicious and cruel.
- C. cautious and glum.
- D. nervous and passionate.

_____ 3. In contrast to Roderick Usher, the narrator presents himself as someone who values
- A. reason.
- B. money.
- C. nature.
- D. a juicy horror tale.

_____ 4. Which passage most underscores the single effect of "The Fall of the House of Usher"?
- A. "There was an iciness, a sinking, a sickening of the heart—an unredeemed dreariness of thought which no goading of the imagination could torture into aught of the sublime."
- B. "Although, as boys, we had been even intimate associates, yet I really knew little of my friend."
- C. "Beyond this indication of extensive decay, however, the fabric gave little token of instability."
- D. "It had been used, apparently, in remote feudal times, for the worst purposes of a donjon-keep, and, in later days, as a place of deposit for powder."

_____ 5. Which choice below presents the core meaning of the following sentence?

One of the phantasmagoric conceptions of my friend, partaking not so rigidly of the spirit of abstraction, may be shadowed forth, although feebly, in words.

- A. The phantasmagoric conceptions partake not so rigidly.
- B. One of the phantasmagoric conceptions of my friend may be shadowed.
- C. The spirit of abstraction may be shadowed forth in words.
- D. One of the phantasmagoric conceptions of my friend may be shadowed forth in words.

_____ 6. Which statement expresses a central theme of "The Fall of the House of Usher"?
- A. Too much contact with the world leads to a distortion of reality.
- B. Isolation of the mind leads to death of the body.
- C. A person cut off from the world can fall prey to irrational fears and mental illness.
- D. The mind cannot affect the body in any way.

_____ 7. Which detail early in "The Fall of the House of Usher" most clearly foreshadows, or hints at, the story's ending?
A. the narrator's memories of Roderick as a boy
B. the narrator's fear of the tarn
C. the narrator's concern for Roderick and his sister
D. the lofty, high-windowed room

_____ 8. Why does the narrator "start" when Roderick Usher mentions "the gradual yet certain condensation of an atmosphere . . . about the waters and the walls" of the House of Usher?
A. The narrator himself felt such an atmosphere when he approached the estate.
B. Usher's idea is so incredible that it frightens the narrator.
C. It gives the narrator his first inkling of his friend's instability.
D. Usher is predicting the destruction of the house in a terrifying way.

_____ 9. What does the speaker in "The Raven" feel when he first thinks that Lenore may be at his door?
A. joy and passion
B. terror and hope
C. relief and pleasure
D. confusion and melancholy

_____ 10. When the speaker describes Lenore as "nameless *here* for evermore," what does he mean?
A. He cannot remember Lenore's name.
B. No one will speak Lenore's name because the angels took her.
C. Lenore is never mentioned in the speaker's chamber because she deserted him.
D. Lenore is so special that she is nameless in the speaker's heart.

_____ 11. Which of these lines most contributes the eerie, hypnotic single effect of "The Raven"?
A. "And the silken, sad, uncertain rustling of each purple curtain / Thrilled me—filled me with fantastic terrors never felt before"
B. "For we cannot help agreeing that no sublunary being / Ever yet was blessed with seeing bird above his chamber door"
C. "'Prophet!' said I, 'thing of evil!—prophet still, if bird or devil!'"
D. "'Be that word our sign of parting, bird or fiend!' I shrieked, upstarting— / 'Get thee back into the tempest and the Night's Plutonian shore!'"

_____ 12. Which of these statements expresses a central theme of "The Raven"?
A. Loss of love causes a person to become bitter.
B. Belief in superstition can be dangerous.
C. Grief can cause hallucinations.
D. Isolation can lead to madness.

_____ **13.** Which choice below presents the core meaning of the following sentence?

> But the Raven, sitting lonely on the placid bust, spoke only / That one word, as if his soul in that one word he did outpour.

    A. But the Raven sitting lonely that one word did outpour.
    B. The raven on the placid bust his soul in that one word he did outpour.
    C. The raven spoke only that one word.
    D. His soul in that one word he did outpour.

Vocabulary and Grammar

_____ **14.** The words "not the least *obeisance* made he" stress the raven's
    A. black plumage reflecting no light.
    B. strange, ungainly walk.
    C. inability or refusal to say more than one word.
    D. refusal to behave respectfully.

_____ **15.** Which word below is closest in meaning to the word *craven*?
    A. dark
    B. cowardly
    C. calm
    D. specious

_____ **16.** The phrase "*equivocal appellation* of the 'House of Usher'" refers to the fact that
    A. the final destiny of the House of Usher is doubtful.
    B. good and evil are equally mixed within the House of Usher.
    C. Roderick and Madeline often speak their family name in a booming tone.
    D. the title "House of Usher" seems to include both the estate and the family.

_____ **17.** Which words in this phrase are coordinate adjectives?

> And the silken, sad, uncertain rustling of each purple curtain

    A. *silken* and *sad* only
    B. *sad* and *uncertain* only
    C. *silken, sad*, and *uncertain* only
    D. *silken, sad, uncertain*, and *purple*

Essay

18. Suppose you had an encounter with Poe's raven. How would you feel? How would you react? How would your response to the raven compare and contrast to that of the speaker in "The Raven"? Write an essay that answers these questions.

19. Some critics believe that the point Poe is making in "The Fall of the House of Usher" is that when creative artists like Roderick Usher completely turn away from the external world and are drawn into the internal world of their imagination, they destroy their ability to create and may eventually destroy themselves. Do you agree or disagree with this interpretation? Write an essay that states your position and supports it with examples from the story.

Vocabulary Warm-up Word Lists

Study these words from the selection. Then, complete the activities.

Word List A

amiss [uh MIS] *adv.* in error; wrongly
    Please don't take my comment <u>amiss</u>, but I think your tie is crooked.

apprehensive [ap ree HEN siv] *adj.* worried; fearful about the future
    Because the teacher said the exam would be difficult, Sandra was <u>apprehensive</u>.

averse [uh VERS] *adj.* opposed to
    Most cats are <u>averse</u> to getting wet.

iniquity [in IK wuh tee] *n.* sin; corruption
    In the Bible, the Old Testament has many passages denouncing sin and <u>iniquity</u>.

instinctive [in STINK tiv] *adj.* prompted by an inborn or natural feeling
    It is <u>instinctive</u> that birds find their way south in the fall.

intellect [IN tuh lekt] *n.* mental capacity
    Terry's <u>intellect</u> allowed her to read at an 8th grade level in the 3rd grade.

ostentatious [aw sten TAY shuhs] *adj.* showy; flamboyant
    Although she is extremely wealthy, Irene is not flashy or <u>ostentatious</u>.

refrain [ree FRAYN] *n.* repeated phrase
    At the end of each stanza of that poem, there was a stirring <u>refrain</u>.

Word List B

amiable [AY mee uh buhl] *adj.* friendly; congenial
    At Donna's party, we enjoyed <u>amiable</u> conversations with lots of friends.

attribute [AT ri byoot] *n.* characteristic; quality or trait
    Concern for students is a valuable <u>attribute</u> in a teacher.

censure [SEN shuhr] *n.* criticism
    The congressman's conduct was so shocking that it provoked official <u>censure</u>.

energetic [en er JET ik] *adj.* active; vigorous
    The senator mounted an <u>energetic</u> campaign to ban smoking in public places.

multitude [MUL ti tood] *n.* large crowd
    There was a <u>multitude</u> of spectators for the Fourth of July parade on Main Street.

placid [PLAS id] *adj.* peaceful; calm
    The sailboat traveled on <u>placid</u> waters all day.

retained [ree TAYND] *v.* held or kept in possession
    In the contract, the company <u>retained</u> the right to alter the terms of the pension fund.

venerable [VEN uh ruh buhl] *adj.* worthy of respect because of age and experience
    In his old age, his colleagues regarded Alvin as a <u>venerable</u> and wise advisor.

"The Minister's Black Veil" by Nathaniel Hawthorne
Vocabulary Warm-up Exercises

Exercise A *Fill in the blanks, using each word from Word List A only once.*

As Kent thought about the math exam coming up the next day, he grew more worried and
[1] _____. He was not [2] _____ to math, but it was not his
best subject. He felt that his [3] _____ was more suited to English and history. He had a(n) [4] _____ feel for language, for characters, and
eventful situations. Numbers, he felt, were comparatively abstract, and he found it
hard to relate to them. Kent had also frittered away some of his precious study time
by staying out at the movies. He did not feel guilty, as if he had been indulging in
[5] _____, but he did consider that he had acted [6] _____.
He could try to fake illness with a(n) [7] _____ display of coughing and
wheezing. He'd be ashamed to do that, though. Bleak as it seemed, he would have to
make "CRAM!" his repeated [8] _____ for the rest of the night.

Exercise B *Revise each sentence so that the underlined vocabulary word is logical. Be sure to keep the vocabulary word in your revision.*

Example: Because the work was so <u>tedious</u>, we greatly enjoyed it.
Because the work was so <u>tedious</u>, we soon grew bored.

1. Meg was strongly repelled by Ben's <u>amiable</u> behavior.
   _____

2. Mike's greatest <u>attribute</u> was loyalty, which was foreign to his personality.
   _____

3. Before bestowing the prize, the principal made remarks in <u>censure</u> of Jay's conduct.
   _____

4. Inez did an <u>energetic</u> workout, performing her routines slowly and without enthusiasm.
   _____

5. Through the telescope on a cloudy night, we could see a <u>multitude</u> of twinkling stars.
   _____

6. The dog had a <u>placid</u> disposition, barking loudly and threatening to bite.
   _____

7. Mr. Lindgren <u>retained</u> a large part of his fortune, giving most of his money to charity.
   _____

8. A <u>venerable</u> advisor has provided reliable counsel for only a short time.
   _____

Name _____ Date _____

Read the following passage. Pay special attention to the underlined words. Then, read it again, and complete the activities. Use a separate sheet of paper for your written answers.

Nathaniel Hawthorne often makes use of the supernatural in his stories. A good example is "Dr. Heidegger's Experiment." In this story, four elderly friends gather at the house of Dr. Heidegger, an old eccentric, who likes to perform scientific experiments. Old age has made the friends underline{apprehensive} and fearful. They have all led unhappy lives, wasting their energy and talents. One of them, for example, has indulged in sin and iniquity so much that he is tormented with pains in both body and soul. Another visitor has been a prosperous merchant, but he has behaved amiss and has lost all his money. A third character is a ruined politician, ostentatious for his corruption. Finally, there is the Widow Wycherly, whom scandalous stories have forced into a life of seclusion.

Dr. Heidegger announces to his guests that he has received a package from an acquaintance containing water from the legendary Fountain of Youth, which is located in Florida. He demonstrates the water's powers by placing a crumbling, withered rose in it. When the flower revives to recover its original freshness, the visitors are convinced. Hardly averse to recovering their lost youth, they eagerly accept Dr. Heidegger's invitation to taste the liquid.

In a remarkable transformation, the visitors become young and vigorous. "Give us more!" is their refrain, uttered again and again. By the third drink, though, their instinctive rivalries get the better of them. The men scuffle over the Widow Wycherly. The vase is overturned and shatters, with all the water trickling away. Suddenly, the characters grow old again.

The reader's intellect may find this story hard to accept, because the Fountain of Youth is a product of myth, not science. On a symbolic level, however, Hawthorne's story is an effective morality tale, underlining the dangers of greed.

1. Underline the words in this sentence that give a clue to the meaning of underline{apprehensive}. Use a word meaning the opposite of *apprehensive* in an original sentence.

2. Circle the words in this sentence that give a clue to the meaning of underline{iniquity}. What is an antonym for *iniquity*?

3. Underline the words in this sentence that hint at the meaning of underline{amiss}. What is an antonym for *amiss*?

4. What are two synonyms for underline{ostentatious}? Use the word *ostentatious* in an original sentence.

5. Circle the words in this sentence that hint at the meaning of underline{averse}. What is a synonym for *averse*?

6. Underline the words in this sentence that give a clue to the meaning of underline{refrain}. Is a *refrain* uttered only once, or is it repeated?

7. Circle the words in this sentence that offer a clue to the meaning of the word underline{instinctive}. What is a noun related to this adjective?

8. Underline the words that give a clue to the meaning of underline{intellect}. What is a synonym for *intellect*?

"The Minister's Black Veil" by Nathaniel Hawthorne
Reading Warm-up B

Read the following passage. Pay special attention to the underlined words. Then, read it again, and complete the activities. Use a separate sheet of paper for your written answers.

Like everybody else, Marcy had grown up hearing the old saying that you can't judge a book by its cover. The saying had a <u>venerable</u> status, one of those ancient bits of wisdom that everyone accepted. Ever since her earliest childhood, though, Marcy had <u>retained</u> a strong doubt about the saying's actual truth. Walk into any high school, she would argue, and you would find just the opposite: people judging each other by their appearance, particularly by their clothes. Like a face, clothes often became an <u>attribute</u> of a person's identity.

In her English class one afternoon, Marcy made a mental survey of how people's clothes revealed their personalities. Tina, the head cheerleader, a peppy, <u>energetic</u> girl, wore a pink mini-dress and big hoop earrings, while a boy named Max, on the other hand, wore black clothes to proclaim his seriousness. In a way, Max's black clothes issued a challenge to Tina's bright attire, inviting disapproval, even <u>censure</u>, as if clothes could pose a threat to other people. But as Marcy looked around, she found that most people chose to wear ordinary clothes—jeans, baseball caps, T-shirts. She guessed that most people wanted to blend in with the <u>multitude</u> of the crowd, appearing not too much like Tina, not too much like Max.

Marcy found it particularly intriguing to look at her English teacher, Mr. Bryant, to see if he too made an effort to express himself through his clothes. She realized that Mr. Bryant arrived at school each day in a tweed jacket and tie, the uniform of a <u>placid</u> man who valued quiet thoughtfulness. She noticed that his encouraging smile became all the more <u>amiable</u> through his wardrobe. The more Marcy thought about it, the more she considered the old saying: The clothes make the man.

1. Underline the words in this sentence that hint at the meaning of the word <u>venerable</u>. What is a synonym for **venerable**?

2. Circle the words in this and the next sentence that hint at the meaning of <u>retained</u>. Use the word **retained** in an original sentence.

3. Underline the words in this sentence that hint at the meaning of <u>attribute</u>. What are two synonyms for the word **attribute**?

4. Underline the words in this sentence that hint at the meaning of <u>energetic</u>. What are two antonyms for **energetic**?

5. Circle the words in this sentence that hint at the meaning of <u>censure</u>. What is an antonym for **censure**?

6. Circle the words in this sentence that give a good clue to the meaning of <u>multitude</u>. Use this word in an original sentence.

7. Underline the words in this sentence that hint at the meaning of <u>placid</u>. What are two synonyms for **placid**?

8. Underline the words in this sentence that hint at the meaning of <u>amiable</u>. Use a word meaning the opposite of **amiable** in a sentence of your own.

Name _____ Date _____

"**The Minister's Black Veil**" by Nathaniel Hawthorne
Literary Analysis: Parable

A **parable** teaches a moral lesson through a simple story about humans. Often a parable leaves out specific details about characters or about the location of the story. This technique makes the story more applicable to all readers. For example, in "The Minister's Black Veil," Hawthorne does not reveal the reason Parson Hooper is wearing the veil because the people's reaction to the veil is the critical part of the parable.

Hawthorne calls "The Minister's Black Veil" a parable because he feels strongly about the moral lesson of the story.

DIRECTIONS: *Look at each of the following excerpts. Then, in the space provided, write how you think the language reinforces the message of the parable for all readers.*

Excerpt	How the Language Conveys the Parable
1. Children, with bright faces, tripped merrily beside their parents, or mimicked a graver gait, in the conscious dignity of their Sunday clothes. Spruce bachelors looked sidelong at the pretty maidens, and fancied that the Sabbath sunshine made them prettier than on weekdays.	
2. At its conclusion, the bell tolled for the funeral of a young lady. The relatives and friends were assembled in the house, and the more distant acquaintances stood about the door, speaking of the good qualities of the deceased . . .	
3. When Mr. Hooper came, the first thing that their eyes rested on was the same horrible black veil, which had added deeper gloom to the funeral, and could portend nothing but evil to the wedding.	

"The Minister's Black Veil" by Nathaniel Hawthorne
Reading Strategy: Draw Inferences About Meaning

When you **draw an inference** in reading a story, you use the surrounding details to make a reasonable guess about what parts of the story mean. To draw thoughtful inferences, look carefully at the writer's description of events and characters and use of literary devices. For example, note Hawthorne's detail as he describes Mr. Hooper's black veil on the Sunday he appears in church.

> Swathed about his forehead, and hanging down over his face, so low as to be shaken by his breath, Mr. Hooper had on a black veil. On a nearer view it seemed to consist of two folds of crape . . . With this gloomy shade before him, good Mr. Hooper walked onward, at a slow and quiet pace, stooping somewhat, and looking on the ground . . .

Based on Hawthorne's description, you might infer that something bad has happened to someone close to Hooper.

DIRECTIONS: *Read the details from "The Minister's Black Veil" in the following chart. Write down what you know from the story and from your own life. Write what you think the author means.*

Details	What I Know	Inference
1. That mysterious emblem was never once withdrawn. It shook with his measured breath . . . it threw its obscurity between him and the holy page . . . and while he prayed, the veil lay heavily upon his uplifted countenance.		
2. It was remarkable that of all the busybodies and impertinent people in the parish, not one ventured to put the plain question to Mr. Hooper . . . Hitherto whenever there appeared the slightest call for such interference, he had never lacked advisers . . .		

"The Minister's Black Veil" by Nathaniel Hawthorne
Vocabulary Builder

Using the Root -equi-

A. DIRECTIONS: *The word root* -equi- *means "equal." Keep that in mind as you answer the following questions on the lines provided.*

1. What would you guess about the sides of an *equilateral* triangle?
   _____

2. Why might the imaginary line around the middle of the earth be called the *equator*?
   _____

3. To what do you think *equity* in the legal system might refer?
   _____

4. What would you guess about the length of day and night on the spring or autumn day called the *equinox*?
   _____

5. What circus performer do you think might be called an *equilibrist*? Why?
   _____

Using the Word List

venerable	sagacious	waggery	iniquity	vagary
impertinent	indecorous	tremulous	obstinacy	ostentatious

B. DIRECTIONS: *On the line before each word in the left column, write the letter of its definition.*

___ 1. venerable   A. characterized by trembling

___ 2. iniquity   B. not showing proper respect

___ 3. indecorous   C. wise

___ 4. ostentatious   D. mischievous humor

___ 5. sagacious   E. commanding respect

___ 6. vagary   F. improper

___ 7. tremulous   G. intended to attract notice

___ 8. waggery   H. stubbornness

___ 9. impertinent   I. an unpredictable occurrence

___10. obstinacy   J. sin

"The Minister's Black Veil" by Nathaniel Hawthorne

Grammar and Style: Varying Sentence Openers

To make writing lively and interesting, it helps to vary sentence openings. Notice how Hawthorne varies his sentence openers in the following passage.

1 The cause of so much amazement may appear sufficiently slight. **2** Mr. Hooper, a gentlemanly person, about thirty, though still a bachelor, was dressed with due clerical neatness, as if a careful wife had starched his band, and brushed the weekly dust from his Sunday's garb. **3** There was but one thing remarkable in his appearance. **4** Swathed about his forehead, and hanging down over his face, so low as to be shaken by his breath, Mr. Hooper had on a black veil. **5** On a nearer view it seemed to consist of two folds of crape, which entirely concealed his features, except the mouth and chin.

Sentences 1 and 2 both open in the most common way, with their subjects (preceded in sentence 1 by the article *The*). Sentence 3, on the other hand, uses inverted order, placing the subject (*thing*) after the verb (*was*). Sentence 4 adds more variety by opening with a participial phrase (*Swathed about his forehead*). Sentence 5 opens in yet another way, with a prepositional phrase (*On a nearer view*).

A. PRACTICE: *On the lines provided, explain how Hawthorne varies his sentence openers in this passage.*

After a brief interval, forth came good Mr. Hooper also, in the rear of his flock. Turning his veiled face from one group to another, he paid due reverence to the hoary heads, saluted the middle-aged with kind dignity as their friend and spiritual guide, greeted the young with mingled authority and love, and laid his hands on the little children's heads to bless them. Such was always his custom on the Sabbath day.

_____

_____

_____

B. Writing Application: *On the lines provided, rewrite the following paragraph so that the sentence openers are more varied.*

The clergyman stepped into the room where the corpse was laid. He bent over the coffin to take a last farewell of his deceased parishioner. His veil hung straight down from his forehead as he stooped. The dead maiden's eyes were closed forever, otherwise she might have seen his face. Mr. Hooper nevertheless seemed fearful of her glance, for he hastily caught back the black veil.

_____

_____

_____

Name _____   Date _____

"The Minister's Black Veil" by Nathaniel Hawthorne
Support for Writing

As you think about your **response to a short story,** choose one particularly dark passage in "The Minister's Black Veil." Think about how you responded to that passage. Enter details about the passage and your response in the chart below.

Response to "Minister's Black Veil"	
Passage I am responding to	
Setting/Characters	
What occurs in passage	
My response/explanation for my response	

On a separate page, write a draft of your response to this story. When you go back to revise your work, be sure you have written clear reasons that show why the passage had such a strong impression on you. Note what your response shows about the kind of literature you prefer.

"The Minister's Black Veil" by Nathaniel Hawthorne
Support for Extend Your Learning

Listening and Speaking

As you plan to write a **monologue** for Elizabeth to deliver to her fiancé asking him to remove his black veil, keep these things in mind:

- Use a familiar tone of address.
- Maintain the Puritan style of speaking with restraint.
- Refer to Elizabeth's history with Mr. Hooper and her hopes for their future.

On a separate page, write a monologue. Present your monologue to the class. You may wish to ask classmates to respond as if they were the minister hearing your plea.

Research and Technology

As you read "The Wedding Knell" by Hawthorne, take notes about how this story and "The Minister's Black Veil" can be compared in preparation for you **oral presentation.** Enter likenesses and differences in the chart below.

A Comparison of Two Hawthorne Stories

"The Minister's Black Veil"

Setting: _____

Characters: _____

_____

Plot: _____

_____

Theme: _____

"The Wedding Knell"

Setting: _____

Characters: _____

_____

Plot: _____

_____

Theme: _____

Now use the information in your chart to prepare a brief oral report to the class in which you compare the two works.

Name _____ Date _____

Enrichment: Art

The painting *Winter Sunday in Norway, Maine* illustrates a New England town much like that in "The Minister's Black Veil."

DIRECTIONS: *Study the painting and then answer the following questions.*

1. Describe the colors in this painting. In general, how do the colors reflect the mood of the story?

_____

_____

_____

2. How is a wintry scene appropriate to the text?

_____

_____

_____

3. What is the effect of the contrast between light and dark in the painting?

_____

_____

_____

4. How are the visual themes of the painting related to the story?

_____

_____

_____

5. How is the painting an appropriate accompaniment to the story?

_____

_____

_____

"The Minister's Black Veil" by Nathaniel Hawthorne
Selection Test A

Critical Reading *Identify the letter of the choice that best answers the question.*

____ 1. In "The Minister's Black Veil: A Parable," what does the word *parable* tell you about the story?
  A. It has animal characters.
  B. It is a science fiction tale.
  C. It teaches a message.
  D. It is frightening.

____ 2. In "The Minister's Black Veil: A Parable," why do the parishioners have such an intense response to seeing the minister's veil?
  A. They feel it is not religious.
  B. They are frightened by it.
  C. They think it is not appropriate.
  D. They feel he must be dying.

____ 3. From this passage in "The Minister's Black Veil: A Parable," what can you infer about the beliefs of the minister's congregation?

> . . . and while he prayed, the veil lay heavily on his uplifted countenance. Did he seek to hide it from the dread Being whom he was addressing?

  A. They trust God.
  B. They ignore God.
  C. They love God.
  D. They fear God.

____ 4. In "The Minister's Black Veil: A Parable," what can you infer that Elizabeth means when she says to Mr. Hooper, ". . . [the veil] hides a face which I am always glad to look upon. Come, good sir, let the sun shine from behind the cloud"?
  A. She loves him and wants to see his face.
  B. She hopes the sun will make him remove the veil.
  C. She hopes the clouds will pass soon.
  D. She thinks Mr. Hooper has a sunny personality.

____ 5. How does "The Minister's Black Veil: A Parable" convey the Puritan attitude toward human nature?
  A. It is full of optimism.
  B. It is full of enthusiasm.
  C. It is full of pessimism.
  D. It is full of forgiveness.

Name _____ Date _____

___ **6.** Who takes care of Mr. Hooper during his final illness in "The Minister's Black Veil: A Parable"?

   A. the couple he married

   B. the town doctor

   C. Elizabeth

   D. a converted sinner

___ **7.** What religious lesson might Hawthorne be teaching through "The Minister's Black Veil: A Parable"?

   A. Our faces show everyone who we are.

   B. Wearing black reminds us that we all die.

   C. People can often see through a veil.

   D. Sin separates us from God and others.

___ **8.** What social lesson might Hawthorne be teaching in "The Minister's Black Veil: A Parable"?

   A. What we look like can be important.

   B. We all have barriers inside of us.

   C. Sadness is always a part of our lives.

   D. Don't be frightened by appearances.

Vocabulary and Grammar

___ **9.** In which sentence is the meaning of the word *tremulous* expressed?

   A. The minister surprised everyone when he began to wear a black veil.

   B. Elizabeth fell to shaking as she realized he would not remove the veil.

   C. The parishioners began to avoid the minister they had once respected.

   D. Mr. Hooper died and was buried without anyone ever seeing his face.

___ **10.** Which of the following sentences begins *without* a subject followed by a verb?

   A. "The sexton stood in the porch of the Milford meetinghouse . . ."

   B. "The afternoon service was attended with similar circumstances."

   C. "She made no reply, but covered her eyes with her hand . . ."

   D. "With this gloomy shade before him, good Mr. Hooper walked onward . . ."

Essay

11. Suppose that the message of "The Minister's Black Veil: A Parable" is that people are sinful. Suppose that the minister wishes to show that sin is a barrier between people and God, people and their loved ones, as well as people and their happiness. Do you think he communicates this message to his parishioners? Are their lives made more religious or spiritual by his wearing the veil, even after his death? Does he inspire them to be less sinful? Write a brief essay to give your opinions about what value Mr. Hooper's actions have on the people of his congregation.

12. In "The Minister's Black Veil: A Parable," the minister's last words include these passages: "Why do you tremble at me alone? . . . I look around me, and, lo! on every visage a Black Veil!" What do you think he means? Write a brief essay to state the inference you can draw from the minister's words.

"The Minister's Black Veil" by Nathaniel Hawthorne
Selection Test B

Critical Reading *Identify the letter of the choice that best completes the statement or answers the question.*

_____ 1. Before donning the black veil, what sort of minister was Mr. Hooper?
   A. outstanding
   B. good
   C. frightening
   D. despised

_____ 2. Over what group does the veiled minister seem to have the most power?
   A. the children of the village
   B. other clergymen in the area
   C. his congregation
   D. souls in agony for sinning

_____ 3. Which statement expresses a central theme of the story?
   A. People are attracted by unsolved mysteries.
   B. People with faith can overcome any hardship.
   C. People are often unwilling to face the truth about themselves.
   D. People who sin should not be forgiven.

_____ 4. "The Minister's Black Veil" is a parable, which means that characters, events, and details of setting
   A. are described in realistic detail.
   B. are gloomy and sometimes terrifying.
   C. are usually historical in nature.
   D. are simplified to teach a moral lesson.

_____ 5. What does the village physician most likely represent in the story?
   A. wealth
   B. religious superstition
   C. logic and reason
   D. human emotion

_____ 6. What message about human nature is most strongly conveyed by Elizabeth's nursing of Mr. Hooper on his deathbed?
   A. Love for someone endures despite what that person does.
   B. Curiosity leads people to do odd things.
   C. Loyalty always leads to learning the truth.
   D. Hard work is seldom rewarded in this life.

_____ 7. What message might be conveyed by the veiled minister at the wedding?
   A. Weddings are joyful, hopeful occasions.
   B. Brides and grooms need to be reminded that they will eventually die.
   C. Secrets between people can destroy trust and love.
   D. The marriage relationship is very difficult.

_____ 8. What does the black veil most likely represent in the parable?
   A. secret love
   B. secret sin
   C. modesty
   D. violence

_____ 9. Based on this story, how would you describe Hawthorne's view of human nature?
   A. naive
   B. pessimistic
   C. idealistic
   D. uncaring

_____ 10. What can you infer about Hawthorne's message from the following passage?

   The next day, the whole village of Milford talked of little else than Parson Hooper's black veil. That, and the mystery concealed behind it, supplied a topic of discussion between acquaintances meeting in the street, and good women gossiping at their open windows. It was the first item of news that the tavernkeeper told his guests. The children babbled of it on their way to school.

   A. Hawthorne thinks that most human beings are respectful of people's differences.
   B. Hawthorne thinks it's important for people to talk about what is happening in their community.
   C. Hawthorne thinks most human beings gossip too much.
   D. Hawthorne thinks children are the worst gossipers.

_____ 11. Based on the rest of the story, what can you infer about the meaning of the following passage.

   "When the friend shows his inmost heart to his friend; the lover to his best beloved; when man does not vainly shrink from the eye of his Creator, loathsomely treasuring up the secret of his sin; then deem me a monster, for the symbol beneath which I have lived and die! I look around me, and lo! on every visage a Black Veil."

   A. It is sometimes good to hide secrets from other people.
   B. Love is not something to be valued.
   C. It is human nature to follow our hearts.
   D. Each person hides his or her darkest secrets from others for fear of what others will think.

Vocabulary and Grammar

_____ 12. Which word most likely identifies what the minister's veil symbolically meant to conceal?
   A. iniquity
   B. vagary
   C. waggery
   D. obstinacy

____ 13. Why is the narrator surprised that the *impertinent* people in the congregation fail to ask Mr. Hooper the reason for the veil?
   A. They command a great deal of respect.
   B. They would be likely to ask questions that might be considered disrespectful.
   C. They are afraid of speaking for fear of appearing disrespectful.
   D. They are interested in appearing intelligent.

____ 14. Which event in the story would best be described as *indecorous*?
   A. the handsome couple getting married
   B. the people rushing out of the church in a confused way
   C. Elizabeth nursing Mr. Hooper
   D. sinners asking for Mr. Hooper when seeking consolation

____ 15. In which sentence does Hawthorne use a participial phrase to vary his sentence openers?

   The cause of so much amazement may appear sufficiently slight. Mr. Hooper, a gentlemanly person, of about thirty, though still a bachelor, was dressed with due clerical neatness, as if a careful wife had starched his band, and brushed the weekly dust from his Sunday's garb. There was but one thing remarkable in his appearance. Swathed about his forehead, and hanging down over his face, so low as to be shaken by his breath, Mr. Hooper had on a black veil.

   A. the first sentence
   B. the second sentence
   C. the third sentence
   D. the fourth sentence

Essay

16. Do you think Mr. Hooper's veil is a form of confession? Is he making a statement? Might it be both? Write an essay describing the conclusion you reach about the significance of the veil. Support your solution with examples from the story.

17. What are the characteristics of the Puritans and their religion as portrayed by Hawthorne in this story? Do you think he has a negative or positive opinion of them? What do you think is his opinion of Mr. Hooper? Write an essay answering these questions.

18. In the story, a lady of the village says, "How strange. . . that a simple black veil, such as any woman might wear on her bonnet, should become such a terrible thing on Mr. Hooper's face!" Write an essay exploring what this statement means in relation to objects and their symbolic power.

Name _____ Date _____

Unit 3: A Growing Nation
Benchmark Test 3

MULTIPLE CHOICE

Literary Analysis and Reading Skills

1. Which of these is a characteristic of the omniscient point of view?
   A. The narrator is a character who takes part in the action of the story.
   B. The narrator refers to himself or herself with the pronouns *I* and *me*.
   C. The narrator provides the thoughts and feelings of many characters.
   D. The narrator provides no commentary about the events in the story.

Read this stanza from a poem by William Shakespeare. Then, answer the questions about it.

> Then to Silvia let us sing,
>   That Silvia is excelling;
> She excels each mortal thing
>   Upon the dull earth dwelling:
> To her let us garlands bring.

2. Which adjective best describes the mood of this stanza?
   A. somber
   B. celebratory
   C. indifferent
   D. angry

3. In the final line of the selection, what are the words *To her*?
   A. a metrical foot
   B. an unstressed syllable
   C. iambic pentameter
   D. a stanza

4. Which lines in this stanza by Emily Dickinson use iambic tetrameter?

> Because I could not stop for Death—
>   He kindly stopped for me—
> The carriage held but just Ourselves—
>   And Immortality.

   A. the first and third
   B. the first, second, and third
   C. the second and fourth
   D. all four lines

Name _____ Date _____

Read this excerpt from Edgar Allan Poe's "The Fall of the House of Usher." Then, answer the questions that follow.

During the whole of a dull, dark, and soundless day in the autumn of the year, when the clouds hung oppressively low in the heavens, I had been passing alone, on horseback, through a singularly dreary tract of country, and at length found myself, as the shades of evening drew on, within view of the melancholy House of Usher. I know not how it was—but, with the first glimpse of the building, a sense of insufferable gloom pervaded my spirit. I say insufferable; for the feeling was unrelieved by any of that half-pleasurable, because poetic, sentiment, with which the mind usually receives even the sternest natural images of the desolate or terrible.

5. Which term best characterizes this selection?
   A. description
   B. summarization
   C. analysis
   D. persuasion

6. The "single effect" created by this selection springs from which of the following literary elements?
   A. dialogue
   B. plot
   C. character
   D. setting

7. What is the defining characteristic of allegories?
   A. They contain dialogue.
   B. They feature animal characters.
   C. They have symbolic meaning.
   D. They are told from the omniscient third-person point of view.

Read this poem by Emily Brontë. Then, answer the questions that follow.

The night is darkening round me,
The wild winds coldly blow;
But a tyrant spell has bound me,
And I cannot, cannot go.

The giant trees are bending
Their bare boughs weighed with snow;
The storm is fast descending,
And yet I cannot go.

Clouds beyond clouds above me,
Wastes beyond wastes below;
But nothing drear can move me:
I will not, cannot go.

8. In the meter of the poem, how many stressed syllables does each line contain?
   A. two
   B. three
   C. four
   D. five

9. To which senses does the description in lines 5–6 appeal?
   A. sight and touch
   B. sight and sound
   C. sound and smell
   D. smell and touch

Read this selection from "Mary and Martha," a short story by Sarah Orne Jewett. Then, answer the questions that follow.

(1) One day, about the middle of November, the sisters were both at home, and sat each by her chosen window, stitching busily. (2) Sometimes Mary would stop for a minute or two, and look out across the country, as if she really took pleasure in seeing the leafless trees against the gray sky, and the band of pale yellow in the southwest, the soft pale brown of the fields and pastures, and a bronzed oak here and there against the blackish-green pine woods. (3) Martha thought it a very bleak, miserable sort of day; her window overlooked the road to the village, and hardly anybody had gone by all the afternoon. . . (4) Mary, as usual, humbly wondered if her sister were lonely and troubled, and if she herself were half so good and tender as she ought to be to one so dear and kind.

10. Which two sentences most clearly indicate that the story is told by an omniscient narrator?
    A. sentences 1 and 2
    B. sentences 1 and 3
    C. sentences 1 and 4
    D. sentences 3 and 4

11. When you break down sentence 2 of the selection above, what is the core of sentence?
    A. Mary would stop and look out.
    B. Mary would stop and take pleasure.
    C. Mary would look out.
    D. Mary took pleasure.

12. From the details in the selection, what do you infer is a main difference between the two sisters?
    A. Mary, though content in most things, is jealous of her sister Martha's beauty and intellect.
    B. Martha is unhappy with her life; Mary is content, except that she worries about her sister.
    C. Martha loves nature and the great outdoors; Mary prefers indoor activities.
    D. Mary is shy and unfriendly; Martha is more outgoing and easier to please.

13. Which of these lessons does the parable most clearly teach?

    A. Beauty is in the eye of the beholder.

    B. Obsession with perfection can be destructive.

    C. You cannot judge a person by his or her physical appearance.

    D. People with their own flaws should not be critical of others.

Read this memorandum. Then, answer the questions that follow.

(1) TO: Eva Berg, Travel Agent
    FROM: Anna Seward, Northwest Cruises
    DATE: 11/5/06
    TOPIC: Alaska Inside Passage cruise

(2) Northwest announces 2007 cruises of Alaska's Inside Passage

(3) • beautiful scenery!
    • bargain prices!
    • luxurious accommodations!

(4) Cruises depart each Saturday from May to October

(5) • Day 1: Seattle   • Day 5: Tracy Arm Fjords
    • Day 2: at sea   • Day 6: Ketchikan
    • Day 3: Juneau   • Day 7: Victoria and Seattle
    • Day 4: Skagway

14. Who has sent this memo?

    A. Eva Berg

    B. Anna Seward

    C. a travel agent

    D. Alaska Inside Passage Cruise

15. How are the features in section 3 of the memo organized?

    A. order of importance (most important first)

    B. chronological order

    C. order of importance (least important first)

    D. enumeration

16. How are the features in section 5 of the memo organized?

    A. order of importance (most important first)

    B. enumeration

    C. order of importance (least important first)

    D. chronological order

Vocabulary

17. Based on your understanding of the prefix *ex-*, what do you do when you *extract* a tooth?
  A. You drill it.
  B. You fill it.
  C. You clean it.
  D. You pull it out.

18. The root *-nym-* can mean "name." Which of these illustrates a *patronymic*?
  A. Scandinavian family names that include the given name of the father
  B. Russian nicknames that include the given name of the mother
  C. Spanish names in which both the father's and mother's family names appear
  D. Chinese names in which the family name appears before the given name

19. Based on your understanding of the prefix *-multi-*, what do you think *multitude* means in this sentence?

At the funeral, Mark Anthony addressed the *multitude*.

  A. a handful of people
  B. a large crowd of people
  C. a serious problem
  D. a cultural event

20. Based on your understanding of the root *-voc-*, what do you think you do when you *vocalize* a problem?
  A. You solve it.
  B. You hide it.
  C. You speak out about it.
  D. You ignore it.

21. Based on your understanding of the prefix *-equi-*, what do you think *equitable* means in this sentence?

They found an *equitable* way to divide the profits.

  A. fair
  B. unfair
  C. clever
  D. confusing

Grammar

22. Identify the adjective clause in this sentence.

Nobody knew if it was she who had placed first in the race on Sunday.

  A. Nobody knew
  B. if it was
  C. who had placed first in the race on Sunday
  D. on Sunday

23. Which sentence uses a participle as an adjective?
   A. The party planner was arranging a large wedding.
   B. My great-great grandparents had an arranged marriage.
   C. We arranged the books alphabetically by author.
   D. Alyson enjoys arranging cut flowers.

24. What word does the participial phrase in this sentence modify?

Marching in the parade, Jeremy was wearing a hat with a shining star on it.
   A. Jeremy
   B. hat
   C. star
   D. it

25. What are coordinate adjectives?
   A. verb forms that are used as adjectives to modify nouns or pronouns
   B. adjectives that follow a linking verb
   C. adjectives of equal rank that separately modify the noun they proceed
   D. a group of words that includes a noun and verb and modifies a noun or pronoun

26. Which of the following sentences contains a collective noun with the correct verb form attached?
   A. A flock of geese migrates together.
   B. The hockey team practice together.
   C. The horse crosses the stream.
   D. The audience clap loudly.

27. Where should a comma or commas be placed in the following sentence?

A burnt orange sun shone on that hot humid Tuesday.
   A. after *burnt* only
   B. after *burnt* and *hot*
   C. after *hot* only
   D. after *hot* and *humid*

ESSAY

28. Think of a story or a narrative poem that is set in the past. Then, write a brief updated version of the poem or story. Convey the same main theme, but add or change some of the details to reflect modern times.

29. Write a piece of literary criticism on a story that you have read. Include a précis of a story, and then explain what you do and do not like about it.

30. Think of a character from a story or novel that provoked a strong response in you. Write a brief character study that includes a detailed description of the character and an explanation of why you find the character memorable. Write in complete sentences, using a variety of sentence structures.

Unit 3: A Growing Nation
Diagnostic Test 4

Read the selection. Then, answer the questions that follow.

Many ancient cultures strived to conquer and map the world's oceans, but the Vikings of Scandinavia were among the earliest and most successful navigators. From the end of the eighth century, these raiders and traders used efficient longships, along with their knowledge of tides, currents, and stars, to explore the rivers of Russia and the Black Sea. Their billowing sails also provided enough wind power for voyages across the freezing Atlantic waters to Iceland and North America. Once they arrived in these distant lands, they attempted early settlements. However, they were seafarers rather than farmers and settlers, and their remote communities quickly failed. Greater success came in England, Scotland, Ireland, and northern France, where they established thriving kingdoms and trading centers.

At the same time, Arab seamen and traders introduced a new era of long-distance sea travel. Their discovery of a sea route to China, via the Strait of Malacca, allowed them to venture to the exotic trading centers of the East, where they purchased silk, spices, and other riches to sell to European traders in Mediterranean ports, such as Venice and Genoa.

1. According to the selection, in what ways were Viking seamen particularly accomplished?
   A. They were extremely successful farmers.
   B. They built brightly decorated ships that were faster than others of the time.
   C. They were extremely skillful at conquering and mapping the oceans.
   D. They set up extremely profitable trading ports along the coasts of the Mediterranean Sea.

2. According to the selection, what helped the Vikings in their voyages of exploration?
   A. their knowledge of tides, currents, and stars
   B. their ability to form and maintain settlements
   C. their inventions, including the spyglass and the compass
   D. their cargoes of silk, spices, and other riches

3. According to the selection, to what faraway places across the Atlantic did the Vikings sail?
   A. Russia and the Black Sea
   B. the Scandinavian countries
   C. North America and South America
   D. North America and Iceland

4. According to the selection, why did the remote Viking settlements fail?
   A. The Vikings were not prepared for the harsh winters they encountered.
   B. The Vikings were not very successful at growing crops and building communities.
   C. The Vikings became homesick and longed to return to Scandinavia.
   D. The Vikings were often attacked by native peoples who feared them as conquerors.

5. According to the selection, what generalization is true regarding the Vikings?
   A. They were cruel conquerors of native people.
   B. They were better sailors than settlers.
   C. They were better farmers than settlers.
   D. They were better sailors than the Arabs were.

6. According to the selection, what important discovery brought wealth to the Arab seamen?
   A. a sea route to the diamond mines of Africa
   B. a sea route to the rich agricultural lands of France
   C. a sea route to China
   D. a sea route to the Black Sea

7. According to the selection, where did Arab and European traders meet to exchange their goods?
   A. port cities on the Atlantic coast
   B. port cities on the Black Sea
   C. port cities along the coast of China
   D. port cities in the Mediterranean Sea

Read the selection. Then, answer the questions that follow.

In medieval Europe, one of the most severe forms of punishment was exile. It forced the guilty person to leave his country for years, and sometimes for the rest of his life. If he lingered, or returned before his sentence had expired, the penalty was usually death. The only contact possible with friends and family was by letter or messenger, and such methods of communication were often unreliable. Therefore, entire families suffered when someone was exiled. To make matters worse, often the entire family's reputation was tarnished by the guilt of the banished member, and laws usually gave officials the power to seize the family's home, land, and personal property.

Wherever the exiled traveled, they were strangers, often regarded with suspicion. Their chances of survival grew slimmer if they had only fleeting knowledge of the new country's language and customs. In addition, their lives were in constant danger from highwaymen and other criminals. The exiled were particularly vulnerable because they traveled alone, and thieves knew that the disappearance of a lone traveler in a strange land would not be readily noticed.

In many societies, banishment was such a terrible, desolate fate that mournful poetry, music, and dramas were written about it. William Shakespeare included banishment in the plots of a number of his plays, including *Romeo and Juliet* and *A Winter's Tale.*

8. Which of the following word pairs contains synonyms?
   A. exile, guilty
   B. exile, banishment
   C. exiled, tarnished
   D. exile, mournful

9. What probably would happen to an exile who returned before his sentence had expired?
   A. He would be banished.
   B. Officials would probably seize his personal property.
   C. He would be sentenced to death.
   D. He would be robbed by criminals.

10. What is the most probable reason that written communications between exiles and loved ones were unreliable?
   A. The messages could not be delivered, as the exile's location was often unknown.
   B. Most exiles could not read or write, so written messages were rare.
   C. There were very few maps of the regions to which exiles were sent.
   D. Many messengers were dishonest, and most post offices were privately owned.

11. What is the most probable reason that laws allowed officials to seize the property of an exile's family?

    A. to make it impossible for the exile to return home

    B. to add further punishment for the crime that the exile committed

    C. to look for clues regarding the crime that the exile committed

    D. to pay for the exile's imprisonment and travel expenses

12. In their new locations, why were exiles often considered suspicious characters?

    A. People were naturally suspicious of strangers.

    B. People had seen the exiles' pictures in newspapers.

    C. Exiles often traveled with highwaymen and other criminals.

    D. Exiles were often related to people who had tarnished reputations.

13. According to the selection, what often proved to be extremely useful to an exile in a strange land?

    A. the ability to write poetry, music, and drama

    B. personal property and land

    C. knowledge of the local language and customs

    D. a map and a compass

14. According to the selection, why were exiles particularly vulnerable to thieves and other criminals?

    A. Because they traveled alone, exiles were often sad and lonely.

    B. Because exiles were strangers, their disappearance might easily go unnoticed.

    C. Because exiles were from another land, they might not understand the local language.

    D. Because exiles were guilty of crimes, thieves did not think it was a crime to rob them.

15. According to the selection, why was banishment a common theme in sad or tragic literature?

    A. Many people enjoyed the bittersweet beauty of sad songs.

    B. Being exiled was a horrible punishment that saddened and frightened people.

    C. Being exiled was an everyday occurrence that many readers could relate to.

    D. Many writers wanted to use the same themes that William Shakespeare used.

Vocabulary Warm-up Word Lists

Study these words from the selection. Then, complete the activities.

Word List A

accumulated [uh KYOOM yuh lay tuhd] *v.* collected; gathered together
  By 6:00 o'clock this morning, six inches of snow had <u>accumulated</u> overnight.

acquiescence [ak wee ES uhns] *n.* agreement
  Paul said his <u>acquiescence</u> to our plan did not necessarily imply his approval.

cringing [KRINJ ing] *v.* fearfully shrinking back or away from
  The dog shrank back, <u>cringing</u> before its owner, who was shouting commands.

dislodged [dis LOJD] *v.* removed; forced from a position or place
  The heavy rain <u>dislodged</u> some of the tiles from our roof.

downcast [doun KAST] *adj.* sad; depressed
  Olga looked <u>downcast</u>, as if she had just suffered a major disappointment.

foreboding [fohr BOHD ing] *n.* prediction or portent, especially of something bad
  Halfway through the movie, a dark musical theme created a mood of <u>foreboding</u>.

imperial [im PEER ee uhl] *adj.* having supreme authority; like an emperor
  In ancient Rome, many of the more important provinces were under <u>imperial</u> control.

outrageous [out RAYJ uhs] *adj.* very offensive or shocking
  We thought their statement was <u>outrageous</u>, worthy of a strong reprimand.

Word List B

admonitions [ad muh NISH uhnz] *n.* warnings
  The Surgeon General gave <u>admonitions</u> concerning the need for exercise.

haughty [HAW tee] *adj.* extremely proud; arrogant
  Richard's sneering remark was good evidence of his <u>haughty</u> attitude.

heroic [hi ROH ik] *adj.* very courageous
  The main character in an epic poem often performs <u>heroic</u> deeds.

inscrutable [in SKROOT uh buhl] *adj.* obscure and mysterious; not easily understood
  With that <u>inscrutable</u> look on his face, we couldn't tell what Max was thinking.

intercept [in ter SEPT] *v.* to stop or interrupt the course of
  You should try to <u>intercept</u> Ken before he leaves on that dangerous journey.

pagan [PAY guhn] *adj.* not religious; heathen
  During the Age of Discovery, most Europeans considered native peoples as <u>pagan</u>.

specific [spuh SIF ik] *adj.* particular; distinct; definite
  Jack's <u>specific</u> problems got him in trouble.

vengeance [VEN juhns] *n.* revenge
  The urge to take <u>vengeance</u> for an injury is natural.

Name _____ Date _____

from **Moby-Dick** by Herman Melville
Vocabulary Warm-up Exercises

Exercise A *Fill in the blanks, using each word from Word List A only once.*

Professional dog training is an amazing field. Trainers who have [1] _____ years of knowledge and experience seem to work wonders with dogs. Animals under their control are not [2] _____ with fear or guilty of [3] _____ behavior. Instead, a trainer has [4] _____ the anxiety and [5] _____ of a poorly adjusted dog and turned the animal into a well-behaved, affectionate pet. How does a trainer secure a dog's [6] _____ and cooperation? Experts agree that there is no substitute for firmness, repetition, and a sensible structure of commands. Trainers cannot afford to seem unhappy or [7] _____ to a dog. Instead, they must always have an optimistic, benign look and a hearty voice. At the opposite end of the spectrum, they must avoid appearing or sounding [8] _____. A dog must know who is boss, but this knowledge must come with benevolent authority, not with tyranny.

Exercise B *Decide whether each statement below is true or false. Circle* T *or* F, *and explain your answer.*

1. *Admonitions* are speeches of praise.
   T / F _____

2. Someone with a *haughty* attitude behaves arrogantly.
   T / F _____

3. *Heroic* behavior typically involves fraud or deceit.
   T / F _____

4. It is hard to figure out the motives of someone who appears *inscrutable*.
   T / F _____

5. If you *intercept* a message, the message eludes or gets away from you.
   T / F _____

6. In the Middle Ages, many Christians were likely to call non-Christian rituals *pagan*.
   T / F _____

7. A *specific* argument is usually general and vague.
   T / F _____

8. If you take *vengeance* on a person, you want to get satisfaction for an injury or wrong.
   T / F _____

Name _____ Date _____

from **Moby-Dick** by Herman Melville
Reading Warm-up A

Read the following passage. Pay special attention to the underlined words. Then, read it again, and complete the activities. Use a separate sheet of paper for your written answers.

Ever since arriving on Cape Cod, Jason had been hounding his mother to go on a whale-watching trip. She worried about getting seasick, having spent a miserable day on a boat twenty years ago in a thunderstorm. Jason persisted, though, doing everything his mother asked. Eventually, he had <u>accumulated</u> such a record of good conduct that his mother couldn't refuse. When he finally got her <u>acquiescence</u>, they made reservations on the *Bayman* and set off the next morning to look for whales.

The sky, gray and ominous, filled the morning with <u>foreboding</u>, as if a violent storm might erupt and send the boat tossing over enormous waves. His mother watched her feet carefully as she climbed aboard, her <u>downcast</u> face showing her nervousness. She seemed terrified as the boat <u>dislodged</u> itself from the dock and set out for the open sea. After that, she sat gripping the edge of her seat, <u>cringing</u> with anxiety each time the boat went over even the smallest wave.

They cruised the waters outside Provincetown for almost two hours without seeing even the slightest trace of a whale. Jason abandoned his mother and stood at the front of the boat, growing ever more impatient for a sighting. It would be <u>outrageous</u> to go to all this trouble and not see even a tail or a fin in the distance. Then, just as he was about to give up hope, the captain shouted. A sperm whale jumped out of the water once, then twice, then a third time. The huge whale dominated the entire ocean, an <u>imperial</u> shape of enormous power. Even Jason's mother stood up to watch him as he appeared once more above the surface.

1. Underline the words in this sentence that give a clue to the meaning of <u>accumulated</u>. Use the word *accumulated* in an original sentence.

2. Circle the words in this and the previous sentence that give a clue to the meaning of the word <u>acquiescence</u>. What is a synonym for *acquiescence*?

3. Underline the words that give a clue to the meaning of <u>foreboding</u>. Use the word *foreboding* in a sentence of your own.

4. Circle the words that offer a clue to the meaning of <u>downcast</u> here. What are two antonyms for the word *downcast*?

5. Circle the words in this sentence that offer clues to the meaning of <u>dislodged</u>. Use a word meaning the opposite of *dislodged* in a sentence.

6. Underline the words in this sentence that give a clue to the meaning of <u>cringing</u>. What is a synonym for *cringing*?

7. Circle the words that give a clue to the meaning of <u>outrageous</u>. Use the word *outrageous* in an original sentence.

8. Underline the words that hint at the meaning of <u>imperial</u>. Is this word used literally or figuratively here?

from **Moby-Dick** by Herman Melville
Reading Warm-up B

Read the following passage. Pay special attention to the underlined words. Then, read it again, and complete the activities. Use a separate sheet of paper for your written answers.

In the mid-nineteenth century, the city of New Bedford in southeastern Massachusetts was the whaling center of America. In New Bedford, there were countless <u>heroic</u> tales of captains, sailors, and ships that had won fame in rough and challenging quests to hunt whales. It is hardly surprising, then, that Melville makes this town the home port of the *Pequod,* the whaling ship of the mysterious, <u>inscrutable</u> Captain Ahab in *Moby-Dick.*

New Bedford was founded in 1652 by settlers from Plymouth Colony. A century later, it had become a fishing community. The deepwater harbor was used by American privateers during the Revolutionary War. These ships would <u>intercept</u> and damage British vessels whenever they could. When the Americans ignored British <u>admonitions</u> to stop these raids, the British sought <u>vengeance</u>. In a <u>haughty</u> display of arrogance, they burned New Bedford in 1778.

The town recovered swiftly, however, and by 1820 it was one of the world's most important whaling ports. In *Moby-Dick*, Melville describes the magnificence of the town's private houses, gardens, and public parks. He also gives a detailed, <u>specific</u> account of the Whaleman's Chapel, where sailors, as well as their wives and widows, would gather for religious consolation. The vast ocean must have seemed to them like a <u>pagan</u> universe, ruled by no caring divinity but rather by the hostile forces of nature. In the Whaleman's Chapel, by contrast, they could recover their faith and cherish the hope that their dangerous journeys at sea would be successful and they would enjoy a safe return. The Whaleman's Chapel, which is now known as the Seamen's Bethel, may still be visited today in New Bedford.

1. Underline the words in this sentence that give a clue to the meaning of <u>heroic</u>. Use the word *heroic* in an original sentence.

2. Circle the word in this sentence that gives a clue to the meaning of <u>inscrutable</u>. What is a synonym for *inscrutable*?

3. Underline the words in this and the previous sentence hinting at the meaning of <u>intercept</u>. What is a synonym for the word *intercept*?

4. Underline the words in this sentence that give a clue to the meaning of <u>admonitions</u>. Use *admonitions* in a sentence of your own.

5. Circle the words in this and the next sentence that give a clue to the meaning of <u>vengeance</u>. What are two synonyms for *vengeance*?

6. Underline the words in this sentence that hint at the meaning of <u>haughty</u>. Use a word meaning the opposite of *haughty* in a sentence of your own.

7. Underline the word in this sentence that gives a clue to the meaning of <u>specific</u>. What are two antonyms of *specific*?

8. Circle the words in this sentence that hint at the meaning of the word <u>pagan</u>.

Name _____ Date _____

from **Moby-Dick** by Herman Melville
Literary Analysis: Symbol

In *Moby-Dick*, many elements take on symbolic meanings as the novel progresses. A **symbol** is a person, place, action, or thing that also represents an abstract meaning beyond itself. In the following passage, for example, the sharks may be symbols of Ahab's destructive behavior or the destructive response of nature to Ahab's mad pursuit of the whale.

> And still as Ahab glided over the waves the unpitying sharks accompanied him; and so pertinaciously struck to the boat; and so continually bit at the plying oars, that the blades became jagged and crunched, and left small splinters in the sea, at almost every dip.

DIRECTIONS: *Read the following passages from* Moby-Dick. *On the lines provided after each passage, identify one symbol that the passage contains and explain what the symbol might represent.*

1. "I came here to hunt whales, not my commander's vengeance. How many barrels will thy vengeance yield thee even if thou gettest it, Captain Ahab? It will not fetch thee much in our Nantucket market."

   "Nantucket market! hoot! But come closer, Starbuck. . . ."

   "Vengeance on a dumb brute!" cried Starbuck, "that simply smote thee from blindest instinct! Madness! To be enraged with a dumb thing, Captain Ahab, seems blasphemous."

   _____

   _____

   _____

2. "The ship? Great God, where is the ship?". . . Concentric circles seized the lone boat itself, and all its crew, and each floating oar, and every lance pole, and spinning, animate and inanimate, all round and round in one vortex, carried the smallest chip of the *Pequod* out of sight.

   _____

   _____

   _____

3. A sky hawk that tauntingly had followed the main-truck downwards from its natural home among the stars, . . . this bird now chanced to intercept its broad fluttering wing between the hammer and the wood: and simultaneously feeling that ethereal thrill, the submerged savage beneath, in his deathgrasp, kept his hammer frozen there: and so the bird of heaven, with archangelic shrieks, and his imperial beak thrust upwards, and his whole captive form folded in the flag of Ahab, went down with his ship, which like Satan, would not sink to hell till she had dragged a living part of heaven along with her.

   _____

   _____

   _____

from **Moby-Dick** by Herman Melville
Reading Strategy: Recognize Symbols

To recognize symbols, take note of any connections an author makes between a person, place, event, or object and an abstract idea or concept. Consider, for example, the following passage:

"Give way!" cried Ahab to the oarsmen, and the boats darted forward to the attack; but maddened by yesterday's fresh irons that corroded in him, Moby-Dick seemed combinedly possessed by all the angels that fell from heaven.

Here Melville connects Moby-Dick to a larger idea by comparing him to "all the angels that fell from heaven," or devils. The connection suggests that Moby-Dick might be a symbol of evil or of the darker side of human nature.

DIRECTIONS: *Read the following passage, which opens your textbook selection from* Moby-Dick. *Then, on the lines provided, answer the questions about the passage.*

One morning shortly after breakfast, Ahab, as was his wont, ascended the cabin gangway to the deck. There most sea captains usually walk at that hour, as country gentlemen, after the same meal, take a few turns in the garden.

Soon his steady, ivory stride was heard, as to and fro he paced his old rounds, upon planks so familiar to his tread, that they were all over dented, like geological stones, with the peculiar mark of his walk. Did you fixedly gaze, too, upon that ribbed and dented brow; there also, you would see still stranger footprints—the footprints of his one unsleeping, ever-pacing thought.

But on the occasion in question, those dents looked deeper, even as his nervous step that morning left a deeper mark. And, so full of his thought was Ahab, that at every uniform turn that he made, now at the mainmast and now at the binnacle, you could almost see that thought turn in him as he turned, and pace in him as he paced; so completely possessing him, indeed, that it all but seemed the inward mold of every outer movement.

1. Which details suggest that Ahab is a symbol?

   _____

   _____

2. With what abstract idea or ideas does Melville seem to connect him here?

   _____

   _____

3. Identify one more thing in the passage that might have symbolic significance.

   _____

   _____

4. Which details suggest that it is a symbol?

   _____

5. What abstract idea or ideas does it seem to symbolize?

   _____

   _____

from **Moby-Dick** by Herman Melville
Vocabulary Builder

Using the Prefix *mal-*

A. DIRECTIONS: *The root* mal- *means "bad." Keep that in mind as you write on the line the letter of the choice that best completes each of these sentences.*

1. _____ is often described as *malodorous.*
   A. Cinnamon
   B. A rose
   C. A squirrel
   D. A skunk

2. A *malnourished* child most likely eats _____ meals.
   A. well-balanced
   B. skimpy
   C. hearty
   D. tasty

3. A *malcontent* probably _____ his or her job.
   A. loves
   B. hates
   C. is puzzled by
   D. never complains about

4. A man with a *malady* has _____.
   A. a disease
   B. great wealth
   C. happiness
   D. an aristocratic wife

5. A woman might be called a *malefactor* if she _____.
   A. gives to charity
   B. teaches math
   C. commits a crime
   D. loves her husband

Using the Word List

inscrutable	prescient	pertinaciously	maledictions

B. DIRECTIONS: *On the line before each word in the left column, write the letter of its definition in the right column.*

___ 1. inscrutable
___ 2. maledictions
___ 3. prescient
___ 4. pertinaciously

A. having foreknowledge
B. holding firmly to some purpose
C. curses
D. not able to be easily understood

from **Moby-Dick** by Herman Melville
Grammar and Style: Agreement With Collective Nouns

A **collective noun** names a group of people, places, things, or ideas. It may be singular or plural. If the collective noun refers to the whole group as a single unit, it is singular. If it refers to individual group members, it is plural.

Singular: The *crew has* finished *its* work on the ship.

Plural: The *crew were* beginning to straggle back from *their* time on shore.

A. PRACTICE: *In each of the following sentences, underline the collective nouns. Also circle the correct word from each pair in parentheses.*

1. The *Pequod's* company (is, are) drawn from many different regions of the world and stations in life.

2. The crew (performs, perform) (its, their) various duties to keep the ship running smoothly.

3. When Ahab waves his hand, the entire crew (disperses, disperse).

4. The team of harpooners selected by the captain (was, were) the best available.

5. At one point a school of dolphins (breaks, break) the surface of the ocean.

6. A flock of birds (flies, fly) overhead, (its, their) appearance taken as an omen.

B. Writing Application: *For each collective noun supplied below, write two sentences using the noun as the subject with a verb in the present tense. In one sentence, have the noun refer to a single unit. In the other, have it refer to individual group members.*

1. herd _____

_____

_____

2. committee _____

_____

_____

3. jury _____

_____

_____

Name _____ Date _____

from **Moby-Dick** by Herman Melville
Support for Writing

As you think about writing a **character study**, think about why Captain Ahab seems to you either mad or great. Also, think about the main events of the selection and how you might summarize it. Enter the information into the chart below.

Summary of *Moby-Dick*/Ahab's Character	
Main Events First Part of Selection	
Main Events Middle Part of Selection	
Main Events End of Selection	
My Opinion of Ahab/ Reasons for My Opinion	

On a separate page, write a draft that summarizes the selection and gives your opinion about whether Ahab is mad or great. When you revise your work, be sure you have included the important events in your summary and that you have justified your opinion with examples from the selection.

Name _____ Date _____

from **Moby-Dick** by Herman Melville
Support for Extend Your Learning

Listening and Speaking

In preparing a **monologue** for Ishmael to deliver to his rescuers, keep these elements in mind:

- Use terms like Melville's that have to do with boats and the sea.
- Use a tone that is similar to Ishmael's.
- Clearly describe the order of events.
- Add descriptive details about the characters.

Make your monologue as dramatic as possible. Then, deliver it to the class as if they are the whalers.

Research and Technology

As you do research for a **report** on whales that face extinction, consult the Internet for field studies, read library books, and analyze interviews. If possible, view natural history documentaries. Enter your findings in the chart below.

Endangered Whales		
Species of Whale	Reasons for Being Endangered	Conservation Efforts/ Successful or Not?
Species of Whale	Reasons for Being Endangered	Conservation Efforts/ Successful or Not?
Species of Whale	Reasons for Being Endangered	Conservation Efforts/ Successful or Not?
Species of Whale	Reasons for Being Endangered	Conservation Efforts/ Successful or Not?

Using additional paper, write a report. Present your written report to the class. Use photographs from the Internet to accompany your report.

from **Moby-Dick** by Herman Melville
Enrichment: Art

You probably know the saying "A picture is worth a thousand words." Whether or not you think this true, you would probably agree that visual art can be a powerful narrative tool. Study Rockwell Kent's pen-and-ink drawings that illustrate the selection from *Moby-Dick*. Then answer the following questions.

1. What does the picture of Captain Ahab reveal about him? How does the use of shadow add to the impression?

   _____

   _____

   _____

2. What feelings do you get from the drawing of Moby-Dick leaping from the surface of the ocean? Explain how details such as the stars and the indication of water convey movement.

   _____

   _____

   _____

3. What theme of the selection does the picture of the whale and the boat express? How does it do this?

   _____

   _____

   _____

4. How do you feel about the use of color to illustrate this selection? Would black-and-white illustrations have been more effective? Why or why not?

   _____

   _____

   _____

   _____

from **Moby-Dick** by Herman Melville
Selection Test A

Critical Reading *Identify the letter of the choice that best answers the question.*

____ 1. In *Moby-Dick,* why does Captain Ahab seek vengeance against the white whale?
   A. The whale keeps escaping his harpoon.
   B. The whale has taken his leg in a struggle.
   C. The whale chases other whales away.
   D. The whale keeps attacking the *Pequod.*

____ 2. How does Ahab persuade the crew to help him find the whale in *Moby-Dick?*
   A. He appeals to their pride.
   B. He appeals to their loyalty.
   C. He appeals to their skills.
   D. He appeals to their greed.

____ 3. In *Moby-Dick,* what does the gold coin symbolize for the crew?
   A. Ahab's fortune from his business
   B. their reward for finding the whale
   C. the *Pequod's* profits from whaling
   D. Ahab's wish to seem better than them

____ 4. In *Moby-Dick,* who continually tries to make Ahab call off his mission of revenge?
   A. Stubb
   B. Queequeg
   C. Daggoo
   D. Starbuck

____ 5. In *Moby-Dick,* what relationship between Ahab and Moby-Dick does this passage symbolize?

   How can the prisoner reach outside except by thrusting through the wall? To me, the white whale is that wall, shoved near to me. Sometimes I think there's naught beyond.

   A. prisoner and jailer
   B. parent and child
   C. builder and wrecker
   D. victim and lawyer

_____ 6. In *Moby-Dick*, what is the symbolic meaning of Ahab having his crew drink from their weapons?
   A. They are promising not to hunt while drunk.
   B. They are toasting Ahab's great leadership.
   C. They are promising to find the white whale.
   D. They are cleaning their weapons for later use.

_____ 7. In *Moby-Dick*, why is it symbolic for Ahab to compare himself with his ship's mast?
   A. Both are part of the whaling ship.
   B. The mast is stronger than Ahab.
   C. Ahab has a leg made of wood.
   D. The whale is seen from the mast.

_____ 8. In *Moby-Dick*, what does the whale symbolize to Ahab in this passage?

   Retribution, swift vengeance, eternal malice were in his whole aspect . . . his forehead smote the ship's starboard bow, till men and timbers reeled.

   A. a force of nature
   B. an important helper
   C. a strong god
   D. a powerful enemy

Vocabulary and Grammar

_____ 9. In which sentence is the meaning of the word *maledictions* expressed?
   A. Ahab vowed to hunt Moby-Dick to the end of his life.
   B. The captain shouted curses at the whale who escaped him.
   C. The *Pequod's* crew grew afraid of Ahab's obsession.
   D. Ahab died without fulfilling his vow to kill the whale.

_____ 10. Which of the following sentences contains a collective noun used as a *plural*?
   A. The crew is made up of experienced whalers.
   B. A flock of gulls follows the ship hoping for fish.
   C. The school of fish divide and swim in different directions.
   D. A team of workers repairs the broken harpoons.

Essay

11. As you read *Moby-Dick,* you encountered many uses of symbols: Moby-Dick, the wind, the ship's mast, the gold coin, the sea, and so on. What do you think the character of Ahab symbolizes? Write a brief essay about how Ahab is used as a symbol, perhaps of a struggle of some kind. Provide at least two examples from the text. Remember that a symbol can have more than one meaning.

12. Do you think Captain Ahab in *Moby-Dick* is a character who is free? Does he act as a free person and think as a free person because he can sail when he wishes? Or does his obsession keep him in a kind of prison? Write a brief essay to give your response to these questions. Use at least two examples from *Moby-Dick* to support your response.

Name _____ Date _____

from **Moby-Dick** by Herman Melville
Selection Test B

Critical Reading *Identify the letter of the choice that best completes the statement or answers the question.*

____ 1. The name of the whaling ship that Ahab captains is the _____.
   A. *Pequod*
   B. *Quarter-Deck*
   C. *Tashtego*
   D. *Nantucket*

____ 2. The white whale against whom Ahab seeks vengeance
   A. never appears.
   B. treats the ship's crew indifferently when he finally appears.
   C. caused Ahab to lose his leg in a previous encounter.
   D. is never seen by anyone but Ahab.

____ 3. Ahab persuades his crew members to chase the white whale by appealing mainly to their _____.
   A. patriotism
   B. hunger
   C. greed
   D. loyalty

____ 4. Ahab's rambling monologues show that he is _____.
   A. practical
   B. uneducated
   C. vulnerable
   D. single-minded

____ 5. What is the chief significance of Ahab's being drowned by his own harpoon line?
   A. It stresses his inexperience as a sailor.
   B. It stresses the idea that obsession and vengefulness are self-destructive.
   C. It stresses the idea that manmade objects are more powerful than nature.
   D. It stresses Ahab's defiance.

____ 6. One of the central themes conveyed in this selection is that
   A. only the strongest survive.
   B. revenge is justifiable.
   C. whaling is indefensible.
   D. human understanding is limited.

____ 7. The selection portrays nature as
   A. sympathetic and soothing.
   B. violent but tamable.
   C. majestic and elusive.
   D. foolish and vengeful.

____ **8.** Which detail in the following passage is most clearly a symbol?

> A sky hawk that tauntingly had followed the main-truck downwards from its natural home among the stars, . . . this bird now chanced to intercept its broad fluttering wing between the hammer and the wood: and simultaneously feeling that ethereal thrill, the submerged savage beneath, in his deathgrasp, kept his hammer frozen there: and so the bird of heaven, with archangelic shrieks, and his imperial beak thrust upwards, and his whole captive form folded in the flag of Ahab, went down with his ship.

    A. the sky hawk
    B. the stars
    C. the broad fluttering wing
    D. the ethereal thrill

____ **9.** Which detail listed in the choices below most clearly suggests that Ahab's footprints are a symbol in the following passage?

> Soon his steady, ivory stride was heard, as to and fro he paced his old rounds, upon planks so familiar to his tread, that they were all over dented, like geological stones, with the peculiar mark of his walk. Did you fixedly gaze, too, upon that ribbed and dented brow; there also, you would see still stranger footprints—the footprints of his one unsleeping, ever-pacing thought.

    A. the familiarity of the planks
    B. the fact that the planks were dented
    C. Ahab's ribbed and dented brow
    D. the comparison relating them to "the footprints of his one unsleeping, ever-pacing thought"

____ **10.** Which of these aspects of nature does the white whale *not* symbolize?
    A. destructiveness
    B. immortality
    C. spiritual comfort
    D. beauty

____ **11.** To Ahab's mind, Moby-Dick symbolizes a wall that
    A. keeps the ship from its business of whaling.
    B. protects Ahab from his own inner thoughts and desires.
    C. must be broken through to reach the truth behind it.
    D. has grown up between Ahab and his crew.

____ **12.** What behavior of Ahab most clearly symbolizes the restlessness and obsessive nature of his thoughts?
    A. his pacing up and down on deck
    B. his offering mugs of grog to the crew
    C. his nailing a coin to the mast
    D. his being hoisted up the mast in a basket

_____ 13. What does the sea probably symbolize in this final sentence from the selection?

> Then all collapsed, and the great shroud of the sea rolled on as it had rolled five thousand years ago.

    A. humanity's power over nature
    B. nature's power over humanity
    C. the goodness of nature
    D. the changeability of nature

Vocabulary and Grammar

_____ 14. Which of these professions most requires a person to be *prescient*?
    A. meteorologist
    B. dog catcher
    C. whaler
    D. fortuneteller

_____ 15. Which word has a meaning most nearly opposite that of *maledictions*?
    A. blessings
    B. lies
    C. curses
    D. pleas

_____ 16. Which of these sentences illustrates correct agreement with collective nouns?
    A. The class were dismissed when the bell rang.
    B. The club are holding an election on Thursday, March 29.
    C. The crew sail for months without making port.
    D. The choir take their seats beginning around 7 P.M.

_____ 17. Which of these sentences illustrates correct agreement with collective nouns?
    A. The class holds different opinions on the subject.
    B. The club enjoys talking to one another.
    C. This crew is the finest that ever sailed a whaling ship.
    D. The choir sings different parts depending on whether they are alto, soprano, tenor, and bass.

Essay

18. Examine Ahab in his role as captain of the whaling ship. In what ways does he seem to be a good captain? In what ways is he a bad one? Answer these questions in an essay in which you support your opinions with details from the selection.

19. At one point Ishmael, the narrator, states, "For with little external to constrain us, the innermost necessities in our being, these still drive us on." Write an essay that shows how this statement applies to one or more characters in this selection.

20. At one point in the selection, the members of the crew gather to hear Ahab describe his goal and persuade everyone else to join him. Why do you think Melville felt that such a scene was necessary? What are some things that the scene accomplishes? Address these questions in an essay.

Poems by Ralph Waldo Emerson
Vocabulary Warm-up Word Lists

Study these words from the selections. Then, complete the activities.

Word List A

brink [BRINK] *n.* the edge of a steep place; the verge
　We were on the brink of departure when we learned that all flights were canceled.

embattled [em BAT uhld] *adj.* in conflict
　The embattled troops stood their ground on the battlefield.

exhilaration [eg zil uh RAY shuhn] *n.* great joy
　When he was notified of his high grade on the exam, Randy felt exhilaration.

harmony [HAR muh nee] *n.* peaceful agreement
　We try to live in harmony with our neighbors by being considerate and respectful.

melancholy [MEL uhn kuhl ee] *n.* sad or sorrowful state
　There was a melancholy sight of dark skies and falling leaves.

misunderstood [mis un der STUHD] *adj.* interpreted wrongly
　Theo felt misunderstood, so he hastened to explain his position more clearly.

reside [ree ZYD] *v.* to live in a certain place
　There are more things to do if you reside in the city instead of the country.

testify [TES ti fy] *v.* to bear witness
　Several eyewitnesses agreed to testify at the trial.

Word List B

blithe [BLYTH] *adj.* happy; carefree
　Even under pressure, Gary remains cheerful and blithe.

contradict [kahn truh DIKT] *v.* to assert the opposite; to deny
　It is not considered polite for children to contradict their elders.

courier [KOOR ee uhr] *n.* messenger
　Patrick gave the package to a courier for delivery.

immortal [i MORT uhl] *adj.* undying; everlasting
　Some teenagers, considering themselves immortal, take dangerous risks.

imparted [im PART uhd] *v.* shared or gave a part of; told; revealed
　Noah imparted the news only to a few trusted advisors.

integrity [in TEG ri tee] *n.* honesty; moral uprightness
　The mayor was re-elected because she was known for her integrity.

occurrence [uh KER uhns] *n.* happening; event
　A total solar eclipse is a relatively rare occurrence.

tranquil [TRAN kwil] *adj.* calm; peaceful
　The thunderstorms passed through quickly, and the weather is now tranquil again.

Poems by Ralph Waldo Emerson
Vocabulary Warm-up Exercises

Exercise A *Fill in the blanks, using each word from Word List A only once.*

The year 1776 was a critical turning point for the [1] _____ Continental
Army under General George Washington. Many thought the Revolution was on the
[2] _____ of failure. A mood of [3] _____ prevailed as
Washington was forced to retreat from New York through New Jersey. Many Loyalists
were known to [4] _____ in New Jersey, which made retreat more difficult. Washington, though, never gave up. He was [5] _____ by the British, who nicknamed him the "fox" for his ability to slip away. The Battle of Trenton in
late December would [6] _____ to Washington's gift for boldness and surprise. When news of the American victory spread, the colonists' mood changed from disappointment to [7] _____, and the revolutionary cause was embraced
with a new, cooperative [8] _____.

Exercise B *Revise each sentence so that the underlined vocabulary word is logical. Be sure to
keep the vocabulary word in your revision.*

Example: Because rainfall was <u>abundant</u>, the newly planted shrubs withered.
Because rainfall was <u>abundant</u>, the newly planted shrubs flourished.

1. Their habitual frowns showed us that our cousins had a <u>blithe</u> outlook on life.
   _____

2. Otis was not afraid to <u>contradict</u> the boss, saying that he completely agreed with her.
   _____

3. Mark served as a <u>courier</u>, stowing the package at his house for several months.
   _____

4. Hercules was thought to be <u>immortal</u>, dying when he was young.
   _____

5. Sam gladly <u>imparted</u> the news, revealing very little of the story.
   _____

6. Known for her <u>integrity</u>, Mayor Zeiss is facing a corruption inquiry.
   _____

7. If an event is described as an <u>occurrence</u>, it has never happened.
   _____

8. The sea seemed <u>tranquil</u>, with heavy waves lashing the shoreline.
   _____

Name _____ Date _____

Poems by Ralph Waldo Emerson
Reading Warm-up A

Read the following passage. Pay special attention to the underlined words. Then, read it again, and complete the activities. Use a separate sheet of paper for your written answers.

Maria had spent her whole life in a poor section of Baltimore, <u>embattled</u> by gangs and street crime. Day after day, as she walked home from the bus stop, she felt a sense of <u>melancholy</u> about the poverty surrounding her, the abandoned buildings and weed-strewn, vacant lots. Everyone seemed to be living on the <u>brink</u> of disaster, just a few days away from losing their apartment or their job. She knew that another world existed somewhere, where people had houses and lawns and plenty to eat. She also knew that the other world wanted nothing to do with people like her. People like her were <u>misunderstood</u>, as if to be poor meant that you must also be a criminal.

Why couldn't people live in <u>harmony</u>, the rich and the poor together, instead of separated? Maria began to envision a world without ghettos, where the vacant lots became gardens, and the gardens drew people from all over the city because of their beauty. It would not matter where you lived—everywhere would be the same, a place where people could <u>reside</u> in safety, with the same comforts. The more she thought about it, the more sense it made. Give people some start-up money—or just give them a loan—and let them rebuild their own neighborhoods. Let them go to City Hall and <u>testify</u> that everyone deserved fresh air, trees, a place to play sports, or just take a walk. Wouldn't everyone's life improve if everyone had the same chance at happiness? The poor would no longer suffer from jealousy, and the rich would no longer feel afraid. Maria believed that this was the true meaning of America. It should be a place of joy, of <u>exhilaration</u>, where everyone had the rights of life, liberty, and the pursuit of happiness.

1. Underline the words in this sentence that give a clue to the meaning of <u>embattled</u>. Use the word **embattled** in an original sentence.

2. Circle the words in this sentence that give a clue to the meaning of <u>melancholy</u>. Use a word meaning the opposite of **melancholy** in a sentence of your own.

3. Underline the words in this sentence that hint at the meaning of <u>brink</u>. What are two synonyms for **brink**?

4. Underline the words in this sentence that give a clue to the meaning of <u>misunderstood</u>. What is a synonym for the word **misunderstood**?

5. Circle the words in this sentence that hint at the meaning of <u>harmony</u>. What are two antonyms for **harmony**?

6. Circle the words in this sentence that offer a clue to the meaning of the word <u>reside</u>. What are a noun and an adjective related to this word?

7. What is a synonym for <u>testify</u>? Use the word **testify** in a sentence of your own.

8. Underline the word that gives a clue to the meaning of <u>exhilaration</u>. Use a word meaning the opposite of **exhilaration** in a sentence.

Poems by Ralph Waldo Emerson
Reading Warm-up B

Read the following passage. Pay special attention to the underlined words. Then, read it again, and complete the activities. Use a separate sheet of paper for your written answers.

Henry David Thoreau, who greatly admired Emerson, became famous for his decision to <u>contradict</u> majority opinions and live a peaceful, <u>tranquil</u> life alone at Walden Pond for two years. Although many people would not thrive in solitude, it is hard not to admire Thoreau for his <u>integrity</u>—he had an utterly honest goal: to find out what really matters in life. During his stay at Walden, he did not let any <u>occurrence</u> or natural event in the woods go unnoticed. No <u>courier</u> brought messages from the outside world to distract Thoreau or detach his concentration from a focus on the essentials of life. In his classic work *Walden,* Thoreau shared his experiences and <u>imparted</u> what he had learned from his experience.

About the same time, there was another, almost opposite experiment in lifestyle carried out by a group of Massachusetts Transcendentalists. This was Brook Farm, located on 175 acres in West Roxbury, which is now in Boston. Started by George Ripley, a former Unitarian minister, Brook Farm aimed to combine thinkers and workers in <u>blithe</u> and peaceful harmony. It was organized somewhat like a corporation, with shareholders who held stock; one of the original members was the writer Nathaniel Hawthorne.

Brook Farm generated an enormous amount of interest among leading intellectuals and writers of the day. Interested visitors included the educational theorist Bronson Alcott, the feminist author Margaret Fuller, and Ralph Waldo Emerson. The community's school was especially notable. Communal living, though, seemed to have many disadvantages. By 1847, after only six years of operation, the experiment was abandoned, and two years later the land and buildings were sold. Brook Farm itself was hardly <u>immortal</u>, but its name lives on because so many distinguished figures were associated with it.

1. Underline the words in this sentence that hint at the meaning of the word <u>contradict</u>. What is a synonym for *contradict*?

2. Circle the word in this sentence that hints at the meaning of <u>tranquil</u>. What are two antonyms for *tranquil*?

3. Underline the words in this sentence that hint at the meaning of <u>integrity</u>. Use a word meaning the opposite of *integrity* in an original sentence.

4. Underline the words in this sentence that hint at the meaning of <u>occurrence</u>. Use the word *occurrence* in a sentence of your own.

5. Circle the words in this sentence that hint at the meaning of <u>courier</u>. What is a synonym for *courier*?

6. Circle the words in this sentence that give a good clue to the meaning of <u>imparted</u>. Use the word *imparted* in an original sentence.

7. Underline the words in this sentence that hint at the meaning of <u>blithe</u>. What are two antonyms for *blithe*?

8. Underline the words in this sentence that hint at the meaning of <u>immortal</u>. What is a synonym for *immortal*?

from **Nature,** *from* **Self-Reliance, "The Snowstorm,"** and **"Concord Hymn"**
by Ralph Waldo Emerson

Literary Analysis: Transcendentalism

Transcendentalism was an offshoot of romanticism that became the philosophy of Ralph Waldo Emerson and several other American intellectuals of his day. Emerson's writings embody the following important principles of Transcendentalism.

A. The human spirit can intuitively comprehend the fundamental truths of the universe.

B. The human spirit is reflected in nature.

C. All forms of being are spiritually united.

DIRECTIONS: *Read these passages from Emerson's essays. Then, on the line provided, write the letter of the principle of Transcendentalism (from the list above) that each passage best illustrates.*

_____ **1.** Nature is a setting that fits equally well a comic or a mourning piece. In good health, the air is a cordial of incredible virtue.

_____ **2.** The currents of the Universal Being circulate through me; I am part or parcel of God.

_____ **3.** The greatest delight which the fields and woods minister is the suggestion of an occult relation between man and the vegetable.

_____ **4.** Nature always wears the colors of the spirit.

_____ **5.** The power which resides in him is new in nature, and none but he knows what it is which he can do.

_____ **6.** Trust thyself: every heart vibrates to that iron string.

_____ **7.** Nothing is at last sacred but the integrity of our own mind.

Name _____ Date _____

from **Nature,** *from* **Self-Reliance, "The Snowstorm,"** and **"Concord Hymn"**
by Ralph Waldo Emerson
Reading Strategy: Challenge the Text

One way to gain more understanding of a work is to **challenge the text**, or question the author's assertions. Here are some guidelines.

- Identify the author's opinions and restate them in your own words.
- Evaluate the examples, reasons, or other evidence the author provides to support his or her opinions.
- Consider other evidence that supports or refutes the author's opinions.
- On the basis of the evidence, decide if you agree or disagree with the author.

DIRECTIONS: *Read the following passage from* Self-Reliance. *Then challenge the text by performing the numbered activities below. Write your responses on the lines provided.*

Society everywhere is in conspiracy against the manhood of every one of its members. Society is a joint-stock company in which the members agree for the better securing of his bread to each shareholder, to surrender the liberty and culture of the eater. The virtue in most request is conformity. Self-reliance is its aversion. It loves not realities and creators, but names and customs.

1. Restate Emerson's basic opinion about society.

   _____

   _____

2. Identify and evaluate the evidence Emerson uses to support that opinion.

   _____

   _____

   _____

3. Provide examples from everyday life to support and refute Emerson's opinion of society.

   Support: _____

   _____

   _____

   Refute: _____

   _____

   _____

from Nature, *from* Self-Reliance, "The Snowstorm," and "Concord Hymn"
by Ralph Waldo Emerson
Vocabulary Builder

Using the Root -radi-

A. DIRECTIONS: *The root -radi- means "spoke" or "ray." On the line after each sentence below, explain how the italicized word reflects the meaning of the root -radi-.*

1. The bride's happiness seemed to *radiate* from her very soul.

   _____

2. The *radius* of a circle extends from the center to the outer edge.

   _____

3. The *radiator* emitted enough heat to warm the entire room.

   _____

4. Professor Diaz transmitted the message across the air waves via *radio*.

   _____

5. *Radioactive* elements emit energy as a result of nuclear decay.

   _____

Using the Word List

blithe	chaos	suffrage	radiant	bastions
connate	aversion	divines	tumultuous	rude

B. DIRECTIONS: *On the line, write the letter of the word that is most nearly the same in meaning as the word in capitals.*

____ 1. BLITHE: **A.** lighthearted **B.** sorrowful **C.** well-lit **D.** gloomy

____ 2. CONNATE: **A.** imply **B.** denote **C.** dishonest **D.** inborn

____ 3. CHAOS: **A.** joy **B.** pain **C.** confusion **D.** silence

____ 4. AVERSION: **A.** attraction **B.** distaste **C.** discrepancy **D.** revision

____ 5. SUFFRAGE: **A.** vote **B.** anxiety **C.** legality **D.** femininity

____ 6. DIVINES: **A.** politicians **B.** clerics **C.** performers **D.** inventors

____ 7. RADIANT: **A.** cool **B.** eager **C.** glowing **D.** moist

____ 8. TUMULTUOUS: **A.** simple **B.** persuasive **C.** momentous **D.** stormy

____ 9. BASTIONS: **A.** villains **B.** soldiers **C.** fortresses **D.** dungeons

____ 10. RUDE: **A.** loud **B.** unrefined **C.** angry **D.** undercooked

Name _____ Date _____

from Nature, *from* **Self-Reliance, "The Snowstorm,"** and **"Concord Hymn"**
by Ralph Waldo Emerson

Grammar and Style: Varying Sentence Length

Nothing is more monotonous than a series of similarly structured sentences of about the same length. Good writers vary sentence length to establish an interesting rhythm that captures the reader's attention. Often they follow a long sentence with a short one:

> The greatest delight which the fields and woods minister is the suggestion of an occult relation between man and the vegetable. I am not alone and unacknowledged.

A. PRACTICE: *For each item, circle the letter of the sentence that would sound better after the sentence in italics.*

1. *Within these plantations of God, a decorum and sanctity reign, a perennial festival is dressed, and the guest sees not how he should tire of them in a thousand years.*

   A. In the woods, we return to reason and faith.

   B. Within the woods where God himself dwells, I as a human being return to reason of the most elemental kind, and I also return also to faith.

2. *Trust thyself.*

   A. Accept your place. Don't fight divine providence. Acknowledge your contemporaries. Join society. Accept the connection of events.

   B. Accept the place the divine providence has found for you: the society of your contemporaries, the connection of events.

B. Writing Application: *On the lines below, rewrite this paragraph to create more sentence variety. Feel free to add new words and leave out insignificant ones, but do not omit any of the facts presented.*

On April 19, 1775, a group of American farmers serving as Minute Men began the American Revolution when they fired at the British at Lexington and Concord, Massachusetts. Some decades later, Ralph Waldo Emerson called the first shot of the Revolution "the shot heard round the world." Emerson used the phrase in his "Concord Hymn," which was sung on July 4, 1837, at the unveiling of a monument honoring the Minute Men's stand.

_____

_____

_____

_____

_____

_____

_____

_____

from Nature, from Self-Reliance, "The Snowstorm," and "Concord Hymn"
by Ralph Waldo Emerson
Support for Writing

To gather material for your critical evaluation of the selection from *Self-Reliance*, enter key points into the chart below.

My Critique of *Self-Reliance*	
Main Ideas of Essay/Beginning	
Main Ideas of Essay/Middle	
Main Ideas of Essay/End	
Emerson's Argument/Summary Statement	
My Opinion/Support from Text	

On a separate page, write a first draft of your critical evaluation. When you revise your work, be sure you have made your critical opinion of the essay clear and have supported it with examples from the selection.

from **Nature,** *from* **Self-Reliance, "The Snowstorm,"** and **"Concord Hymn"**
by Ralph Waldo Emerson
Support for Extend Your Learning

Listening and Speaking

Prepare to write a **public service announcement** that urges people to resist conformity. Use arguments from Emerson's *Self-Reliance* as well as your own ideas. Organize your ideas using the following techniques:

- Inductive reasoning (use specific details to draw a general conclusion)
- Deductive reasoning (build an argument on generally accepted principles)

On a separate page, write your announcement. Begin with a catchy phrase, such as Emerson's "Trust thyself," or "To be great is to be misunderstood." You can also use a phrase of your own creation. When you have completed your announcement, record it and present it to the class.

Technology and Research

To write a **profile** of someone who was both great and misunderstood, choose one of the following and do library and Internet research: Socrates, Pythagoras, Jesus, Joan of Arc, of someone of your choosing. Fill in the biography chart below.

[NAME]—Great and Misunderstood	
Historical Person	
Basic Facts of Life	
Why misunderstood in lifetime	
Why important today	

On a separate page, write a profile of the person you have selected. Share your profile with the rest of the class. Compare it with the profiles of other students who have chosen the same person.

Name _____ Date _____

from Nature, *from* Self-Reliance, "The Snowstorm," and "Concord Hymn"
by Ralph Waldo Emerson
Enrichment: Local Landmarks

Like the statue of the Minute Men commemorated in "Concord Hymn," monuments honoring historic figures and events can be found in just about every town and city in the United States. Locate one such memorial in your own area. Then, on the lines provided, answer the following questions about the monument. To answer, you may need to visit the monument and do additional research at a local library or historical society. If an answer is unavailable, write "unknown" or "does not apply."

1. Where is the monument located?

   _____

2. What form does the monument take—statue, plaque, or other?

   _____

3. What occasion, person, or group does the monument celebrate?

   _____

4. When was the monument erected?

   _____

5. Who erected the monument?

   _____

6. What inscription, if any, accompanies the monument?

   _____

7. What visual symbols, if any, does the monument include?

   _____

8. How is the monument like and unlike the monument honored in "Concord Hymn"?

   _____

   _____

9. In the space below or on a separate piece of paper, write your own poem or brief speech that could have accompanied the dedication of the monument. If possible, provide a photograph, drawing, or model of the monument to share with the class as you read your tribute aloud.

   _____

   _____

   _____

   _____

from Nature, *from* Self-Reliance, "The Snowstorm," and "Concord Hymn"
by Ralph Waldo Emerson
Selection Test A

Critical Reading *Identify the letter of the choice that best answers the question.*

____ 1. How does a reader challenge any text?
   A. by questioning the writer's opinions
   B. by proofreading the material for errors
   C. by agreeing with the writer's opinions
   D. by rereading the text for clarity

____ 2. What is a basic Transcendentalist idea found in the selection from *Nature*?
   A. Nature is cruel and indifferent.
   B. Nature and humans are connected.
   C. Nature must be studied to be appreciated.
   D. Nature is apart from the human world.

____ 3. Which of these suggests a meaning for Emerson's words from *Nature:* "In the woods is perpetual youth"?
   A. Only young people like to walk in the woods.
   B. People feel refreshed and young in the woods.
   C. The woods attracts those who don't like to grow up.
   D. The natural world is found only in the woods.

____ 4. Which of the following expresses a key idea of the selection from *Self-Reliance*?
   A. Be guided by the will of the majority.
   B. It is wise to try to be like others.
   C. The individual mind is the only guide.
   D. Social customs are necessary for peace.

____ 5. Which of these character traits, as described in *Self-Reliance*, is a key element of Transcendentalism?
   A. being like others when possible
   B. teaching others to be like you
   C. always being your own person
   D. trying to become a genius

___ 6. In "Concord Hymn," what does Emerson mean by "the shot heard round the world"?

A. a battle fought with very large and noisy weapons

B. a battle written about in many foreign newspapers

C. the opening battle of the Revolutionary War

D. a battle farmers wrote about to their European relatives

___ 7. Which Transcendentalist belief is reflected in this passage from "Concord Hymn"?

Spirit, that made those heroes dare / To die, and leave their children free, / Bid Time and Nature gently spare / The shaft we raise to them and thee.

A. the importance of the individual

B. the unity of nature and humanity

C. the limitation of human senses

D. the presence of an Over-Soul

___ 8. In "The Snowstorm," which element of Transcendentalism does Emerson depict by comparing the north wind to a human being?

A. the seeking of truth

B. the unity of humans and nature

C. the importance of self-reliance

D. the limitation of human senses

Vocabulary and Grammar

___ 9. In which of the following sentences is the meaning of the word *aversion* expressed?

A. To be self-reliant is to trust one's own heart and experiences.

B. Many great men have also been misunderstood.

C. The conformist is hostile to the person who respects individuality.

D. The world will support a person who acts with integrity.

___ 10. In which of the following pairs is a long sentence followed by a shorter sentence that emphasizes the material in the first sentence?

A. "There I feel that nothing can befall me in life—no disgrace, no calamity (leaving me my eyes), which nature cannot repair. Standing on the bare ground—my head bathed by the blithe air and uplifted into infinite space—all mean egotism vanishes."

B. "I am the lover of uncontained and immortal beauty. In the wilderness, I find something more dear and connate than in the streets or villages."

C. "I am not alone and unacknowledged. They nod to me, and I to them."

D. "In the woods, too, a man casts off his years, as the snake his slough, and at what period soever of life is always a child. In the woods is perpetual youth."

Essay

11. In *Self-Reliance,* does Emerson express respect for the expectations of society, or does he criticize society's expectations? Write a brief essay to give your description of Emerson's position. Use at least two examples from the selection.

12. As a Transcendentalist, Emerson believed in the deep connection between humans and the natural world. How does he express this belief in the poem "The Snow-storm"? Write a brief essay to explain his belief. Use at least two examples from the poem to support your explanation.

Name _____ Date _____

Selection Test B

Critical Reading *Identify the letter of the choice that best completes the statement or answers the question.*

____ 1. With which statement would you expect Transcendentalists to agree?
   A. There is no fundamental reality beyond the physical world.
   B. Human beings have less potential when they act independently.
   C. There is a spiritual relationship between humanity and nature.
   D. People should strive so that their natural souls do not become part of an oversoul.

____ 2. "Concord Hymn" was written to celebrate
   A. music and poetry.
   B. a monument to the Revolution.
   C. Massachusetts.
   D. the end of the Civil War.

____ 3. Readers challenge a writer's text when they
   A. refuse to read.
   B. lend the text to others.
   C. question the writer's opinions.
   D. proofread articles to make them more accurate.

____ 4. Which statements about Transcendentalism are accurate?
   I.   Transcendentalism was an intellectual movement.
   II. Transcendentalism was a largely European movement.
   III. Transcendentalists were interested in the human spirit.
   IV. Transcendentalists thought that an exploration of nature helped people understand universal truths.
   A. I and II only
   B. II and III only
   C. I, II, III, and IV
   D. I, III, and IV only

____ 5. How might a reader challenge the following text from *Self-Reliance*?
   Trust thyself: every heart vibrates to that iron string.

   A. The reader might reflect on personal experience to judge the statement.
   B. The reader might show that the word *thyself* is archaic, or outdated.
   C. The reader might defend the statement because it is written by a famous American philosopher.
   D. The reader might research the facts on how the heart functions.

____ 6. Which view of nature does Emerson take?
   A. Nature is indifferent to human suffering.
   B. Nature must be studied and dissected.
   C. Urban dwellers have little conception of the cruelty of nature.
   D. Nature can inspire the human spirit.

_____ 7. Which of these quotations reflects a key idea of Transcendentalism?
   A. "Nothing is at last sacred but the integrity of your own mind."
   B. "The virtue in most request is conformity."
   C. "With consistency a great soul has simply nothing to do."
   D. "To be great is to be misunderstood."

_____ 8. Which of these statements best characterizes the central idea of *Self-Reliance*?
   A. Meekness is the virtue that fosters self-awareness.
   B. Rely on your own instincts.
   C. Social customs serve a valuable purpose.
   D. Cruelty may be necessary to achieve philosophical goals.

_____ 9. Emerson's romanticism is most clearly displayed in his
   A. careful descriptions of nature.
   B. exaggerated sense of loneliness.
   C. logically constructed arguments.
   D. reliance on emotional truth.

_____ 10. In *Nature*, Emerson writes, "Yet it is certain that the power to produce this delight does not reside in nature, but in man, or in a harmony of both." What philosophy does this statement support?
   A. materialism
   B. Transcendentalism
   C. feminism
   D. creationism

_____ 11. In *Self-Reliance*, Emerson writes that society "loves not realities and creators, but names and customs." Which of these adjectives best reflects Emerson's attitude in that statement?
   A. disapproving
   B. accepting
   C. encouraging
   D. forgiving

_____ 12. Why does Emerson allude to individuals such as Socrates, Jesus, and Galileo in *Self-Reliance*?
   A. to suggest that they agreed with his philosophy
   B. to encourage readers to learn about historical figures
   C. to inspire readers through the example of their struggles
   D. to question their contribution to society

_____ 13. Which of these statements could be used to challenge the text of a written work?
   A. The author presents a thorough analysis of the subject.
   B. The author constructs a rational defense of the position.
   C. The author cites excellent research.
   D. The author expresses opinions as if they were facts.

Unit 3 Resources: A Growing Nation
133

Vocabulary and Grammar

____ 14. Which pair of words expresses a relationship that is most similar to the relationship of these words in capital letters?

SUN : RADIANT ::

A. warm : hot
B. glowing : moon

C. star : small
D. perfume : fragrant

____ 15. Writers vary sentence lengths primarily to

A. increase the pleasure they take in writing.
B. sustain reader interest.

C. cut down on time spent in keyboarding.
D. maintain a steady, monotonous rhythm.

____ 16. Which word below is most nearly *opposite* in meaning from the italicized word in this statement?

He has an *aversion* to joining the team.

A. plan
B. liking

C. distaste
D. hope

____ 17. Which word below can be substituted for the italicized word in this statement?

Modern philosophers theorize that there may be order in *chaos*.

A. disorder
B. nature

C. pain
D. self-reliance

Essay

18. Write an essay in which you describe two examples from Emerson's essay *Nature* that suggest a relationship between the human spirit and nature.

19. In "Concord Hymn" Emerson writes, "Here once the embattled farmers stood, / And fired the shot heard round the world." In *Nature* he writes, "The name of the nearest friend sounds then foreign and accidental: to be brothers, to be acquaintances, master or servant, is then a trifle and a disturbance." Explain the meanings of these passages, and then consider how each of them supports or does not support the Transcendentalists' ideal of an oversoul.

20. Two principal ideas of Transcendentalism are the importance of the individual and the concept of the oversoul flowing from the relationship between the natural world and the human spirit. Do you think that these two beliefs support or conflict with each other? Use examples from Emerson's writings to support your evaluation.

Name _____ Date _____

Gretel Ehrlich Introduces from *Walden* by Henry David Thoreau

DIRECTIONS: *Use the space provided to answer the questions.*

1. At first, why was Thoreau's landscape at Walden Pond unfamiliar to Ehrlich?

   _____

   _____

2. What examples from *Walden* does Ehrlich use to support her assertion that the heart of an essay is "an attempt to understand the nature of things"?

   _____

   _____

   _____

3. **A.** In her commentary, Ehrlich stresses Thoreau's philosophical idea that "life is change." What details does Ehrlich cite to support this idea?

   _____

   _____

   B. Do you agree with the claim that "life is change"? Briefly explain why or why not.

   _____

   _____

4. According to Ehrlich, how would Thoreau advise us to cope with the speed and complexity of modern life?

   _____

   _____

5. Explain what Thoreau means by the "auroral character."

   _____

   _____

6. Do you believe that Thoreau was right in encouraging us to "march to a different drummer" if that's where our destiny takes us? Briefly explain your opinion.

   _____

   _____

   _____

7. What questions about Thoreau's *Walden* does Ehrlich's commentary raise in your mind at this point?

   _____

   _____

   _____

Name _____ Date _____

Gretel Ehrlich
Listening and Viewing

Segment 1: Meet Gretel Ehrlich
- Why does Gretel Ehrlich recommend traveling to other countries?
- What have you learned from either moving or visiting a place different from your hometown?

_____

_____

_____

_____

Segment 2: Gretel Ehrlich Introduces *Walden* by Henry David Thoreau
- How has Gretel Ehrlich's writing been influenced by Thoreau?

_____

_____

_____

_____

Segment 3: The Writing Process
- Why does Gretel Ehrlich believe it is important to constantly record one's observations and thoughts by taking notes?
- What method of collecting information do you rely on when writing?

_____

_____

_____

_____

Segment 4: The Rewards of Writing
- What does Gretel Ehrlich believe is the obligation of a writer?
- What insights about humanity do you think you could gain by reading books about other cultures?

_____

_____

_____

_____

Study these words from the selections. Then, complete the activities.

Word List A

anticipated [an TIS uh payt uhd] *v.* expected
The storm was worse than the weather forecasters had <u>anticipated</u>.

calculation [kal kyoo LAY shuhn] *n.* precise reckoning
Mario realized that a simple <u>calculation</u> would give him the answer.

cluttered [KLUT uhrd] *adj.* crowded; congested
Jimmy <u>cluttered</u> his room with books and newspapers.

enterprises [ENT uhr pryz uhz] *n.* undertakings; business ventures
Restaurants are difficult <u>enterprises</u> to run, requiring long hours of hard work.

essentially [uh SEN shuhl ee] *adv.* basically
The corner lot was <u>essentially</u> bare, with just one tree on the property.

external [ek STERN uhl] *adj.* outer
That medicine is for <u>external</u> use only.

premises [PREM is uhs] *n.* grounds; piece of real estate
Lana lived in gorgeous <u>premises</u>—a lavish mansion overlooking the bay.

superfluous [soo PER floo uhs] *adj.* more than is needed; excessive
You can say all you need to in a brief speech; anything more is <u>superfluous</u>.

Word List B

conformity [kuhn FORM uh tee] *n.* action according to customs or rules
The mayor brought the municipal ordinance into <u>conformity</u> with state law.

inherent [in HER uhnt] *adj.* natural; innate; inborn
The survival instinct is an <u>inherent</u> part of human nature.

mode [MOHD] *n.* manner or way of acting
As a manager, Sam is very excitable and often operates in crisis <u>mode</u>.

piety [PY uh tee] *n.* devotion to religious duties and practices
Attending church every day, Ms. Ramirez was much respected for her <u>piety</u>.

restricted [ree STRIK tuhd] *v.* limited
The new law <u>restricted</u> the use of cell phones by people driving a motor vehicle.

semblance [SEM bluhns] *n.* outward form or appearance
Under a <u>semblance</u> of calm, Sam was terrified.

shun [SHUN] *v.* to avoid consistently; to keep away from
Because of Brad's dishonesty, many of his classmates decided to <u>shun</u> him.

transmit [tranz MIT] *v.* to send; to convey; to pass along
We used e-mail to <u>transmit</u> to our friends the news of our arrival in London.

Selections by Henry David Thoreau
Vocabulary Warm-up Exercises

Exercise A *Fill in the blanks, using each word from Word List A only once.*

Writing in the mid-nineteenth century, Thoreau believed that American life was far too
[1] _____, and he urged his readers to "simplify" their lives. We should try
to focus on the [2] _____ important, inner issues, he thought,
rather than on [3] _____ things or material possessions. The
[4] _____ in which one lives don't matter as much as *how* life is lived.
Testing his theories at Walden Pond, Thoreau recognized that such items as fine
clothes, fancy food, and newspapers are really [5] _____, since they don't
help us to live better. In the [6] _____ of what really matters in life, one
wonders what Thoreau would say if he could have [7] _____ the break-
neck pace and technological quality of American life today. How, for example, would he
have reacted to such [8] _____ as the World Wide Web, the space shuttle,
and electric cars?

Exercise B *Decide whether each statement below is true or false. Circle* T *or* F, *and explain
your answer.*

1. If you act in *conformity* with others, you can be described as unconventional.
   T / F _____

2. Something *inherent* can be described as topical, accidental, or superficial.
   T / F _____

3. Commuter railroad trains are one *mode* of public transportation.
   T / F _____

4. *Piety* is a sign of irreverence or disrespect.
   T / F _____

5. If your privileges are *restricted*, they have been increased or enhanced.
   T / F _____

6. A clever lie may have the *semblance* of truth.
   T / F _____

7. If you *shun* another person's company, you are at pains to seek out him or her.
   T / F _____

8. To *transmit* a message is to revoke it or call it back.
   T / F _____

Name _____ Date _____

Read the following passage. Pay special attention to the underlined words. Then, read it again, and complete the activities. Use a separate sheet of paper for your written answers.

There were only two days left before the Wilderness Club set out for its annual hike. That night, the leader, Mr. Simms, had everyone come to a meeting at the school gym. To enter the <u>premises</u>, hikers had to bring with them a backpack loaded with everything they thought they would need for the week-long trek through the mountains.

Dennis showed up with a pack full of canned spaghetti, soda, and a portable TV. He had not <u>anticipated</u> how difficult it would be to carry such a heavy pack on his back for seven days. Mr. Simms took one look at his <u>cluttered</u> pack and told him to take everything out and start from scratch.

"The first rule of backpacking is that anything <u>superfluous</u>—anything you don't need—has to be left behind," said Mr. Simms.

Dennis unloaded his pack. He realized how few comforts he would be allowed on this trip. It would not be one of those fun-filled <u>enterprises</u> he was used to, when the trip was made easy by snacks and entertainment. This trip would involve hard days of hiking, crossing rivers, navigating boulder fields, then pitching a tent in cold weather, possibly even in snow. Mr. Simms went to the blackboard and wrote out a <u>calculation</u> that showed how much weight you could carry on your back, according to how much you weighed. Then he held up a rectangle of folded-up plastic, a rain poncho, that weighed almost nothing.

"This little item is all you need to protect you from rain, snow, hail: all the <u>external</u> elements that can seep into your skin and your pack on a hike in bad weather."

He had many other words of advice. However, Dennis learned that, <u>essentially</u>, the less you brought, the better.

1. Underline the words in this and the previous sentence that give clues to the meaning of <u>premises</u>. Use the word *premises* in an original sentence.

2. Circle the words that give a clue to the meaning of <u>anticipated</u>. What are two synonyms for *anticipated*?

3. Underline the words in this and the previous sentence that give clues to the meaning of <u>cluttered</u>. Name a synonym for *cluttered*.

4. Circle the words that hint at the meaning of <u>superfluous</u>. Use a word meaning the opposite of *superfluous* in a sentence of your own.

5. Circle the words that offer clues to the meaning of <u>enterprises</u>. What is a synonym for *enterprises*?

6. Underline the words that give a clue to the meaning of <u>calculation</u>. Is a *calculation* normally approximate or precise?

7. Circle the words that give a clue to the meaning of <u>external</u>. Use a word meaning the opposite of *external* in a sentence.

8. Underline the words that hint at the meaning of <u>essentially</u>. Use *essentially* in an original sentence.

Name _____ Date _____

Read the following passage. Pay special attention to the underlined words. Then, read it again, and complete the activities. Use a separate sheet of paper for your written answers.

One of Thoreau's most prominent qualities was his individualism. He felt that it is an <u>inherent</u> duty of human beings to resist <u>conformity</u>. "If a man does not keep pace with his companions," Thoreau wrote in *Walden,* "perhaps it is because he hears a different drummer. Let him step to the music which he hears, however measured or far away."

It was this approach or <u>mode</u> of thinking that inspired Thoreau in his essay "Civil Disobedience." Here Thoreau argues that it is not wrong to disobey an unjust law or policy, especially a law that has wrongly <u>restricted</u> or limited human rights.

Few of Thoreau's readers at the time could have anticipated that his philosophy would directly <u>transmit</u> a set of beliefs to two of the most important men of the twentieth century, Mahatma Gandhi and Martin Luther King, Jr. As an Indian lawyer living in South Africa, Gandhi developed a strategy of nonviolent resistance to the government. The authorities were pursuing a racist policy of discrimination. Back in India, Gandhi believed that there could be no shade or <u>semblance</u> of freedom and dignity for his own people if India's British rulers were allowed to arrest and jail Indians without trial. He called on all Indians to <u>shun</u> work, staying away from their jobs in a massive general strike. Gandhi's strategy of nonviolent resistance, shaped by Thoreau's ideas, set India on the road to independence.

Martin Luther King, in turn, was profoundly influenced by the ideas of both Thoreau and Gandhi. He regarded these men with a reverence that bordered on <u>piety</u>. King spent six weeks in India in early 1959, specifically to learn more about Gandhi. King used ideas that can be traced through Gandhi back to Thoreau. He thus made nonviolent resistance a fundamental element of the American Civil Rights Movement.

1. Underline the words in this sentence that give a clue to the meaning of <u>inherent</u>. Use the word *inherent* in an original sentence.

2. Circle the words in this and the next sentence that give a clue to the meaning of <u>conformity</u>. From what verb is this noun formed?

3. Underline the words in this sentence hinting at the meaning of <u>mode</u>. What is a synonym for *mode*?

4. Underline the words in this sentence that give a clue to the meaning of <u>restricted</u>. What are two antonyms for *restricted*?

5. Circle the words in this sentence that give a clue to the meaning of <u>transmit</u>. What are two synonyms for *transmit*?

6. Underline the words in this sentence that hint at the meaning of <u>semblance</u>. What is a synonym for *semblance*?

7. Underline the words in this sentence that give a clue to the meaning of <u>shun</u>. Use a word meaning the opposite of *shun* in a sentence of your own.

8. Circle the words in this sentence that hint at the meaning of the word <u>piety</u>. What is an adjective formed from this noun?

from **Walden** and *from* **Civil Disobedience** by Henry David Thoreau
Literary Analysis: Style

Readers should look not only at what a writer has to say but also at how the writer says it. The way a writer puts thoughts into words is called **style.** Following are some important elements of style and some questions useful in analyzing a writer's style.

- **Choice of words:** Does the writer choose simple and direct words or words that are more complex and formal?
- **Length of sentences:** Does the writer make frequent use of long or short sentences? Does the sentence length vary?
- **Type and structure of sentences:** Does the writer use a fair amount of questions or commands? Many simple sentences, or compound-complex sentences? Does the writer always open with the subject of a sentence or vary sentence beginnings?
- **Rhythm:** Does the writer create an internal rhythm by repeating words or ideas from sentence to sentence?
- **Use of literary devices:** Does the writer use vivid imagery and strong similes, metaphors, and other figures of speech?

DIRECTIONS: *Read this passage from* Walden. *Then, on the lines below the passage, analyze the different elements of Thoreau's style.*

To my imagination it retained throughout the day more or less of this auroral character, reminding me of a certain house on a mountain which I had visited the year before. This was an airy and unplastered cabin, fit to entertain a traveling god, and where a goddess might trail her garments. The winds which passed over my dwelling were such as sweep over the ridges of mountains, bearing the broken strains, or celestial parts only, of terrestrial music.

1. Word choice: _____

   _____

2. Sentence length: _____

   _____

3. Sentence type/structure: _____

   _____

   _____

4. Rhythm: _____

   _____

5. Literary devices: _____

   _____

   _____

from **Walden** and *from* **Civil Disobedience** by Henry David Thoreau

Reading Strategy: Evaluate the Writer's Statement of Philosophy

In both *Walden* and *Civil Disobedience,* Thoreau expresses his **philosophy,** the system of beliefs and values that guided his life and actions. As you read, you should decide whether you agree with Thoreau's philosophy. To evaluate Thoreau's philosophy, note his main ideas and the evidence he uses to support those ideas. Then evaluate his ideas and evidence by comparing them with your own life experiences. Organize your evaluation in the following chart.

Thoreau's Main Ideas	
Thoreau's Evidence	
My Experiences	
Evaluation	

Name _____ Date _____

from **Walden** and *from* **Civil Disobedience** by Henry David Thoreau
Vocabulary Builder

Using the Root *-flu-*

A. DIRECTIONS: *The root -flu- means "flow." Using that information, write on the line the letter of the choice that best completes each sentence.*

____ 1. If Laura shows *fluency* in Russian,
    A. she has little knowledge of Russian.
    B. she has studied Russian but cannot master it.
    C. she speaks it easily.

____ 2. In an *affluent* society,
    A. many people have and spend money.
    B. most people are very poor.
    C. most people earn good money but refuse to spend it.

Using the Word List

dilapidated	superfluous	magnanimity	posterity
sublime	evitable	expedient	alacrity

B. DIRECTIONS: *Circle the letter of the choice that best completes each sentence.*

1. The building was so dilapidated that the city wanted to have it
    A. demolished.   B. publicized.   C. photographed.

2. Anna saved all of her war memorabilia for posterity, hoping to show it eventually to her
    A. neighbors.   B. parents.   C. grandchildren.

3. Her novels include a fair amount of superfluous information, making them rather
    A. easy to read.   B. time consuming.   C. melancholy.

4. The city's architecture was absolutely sublime, so viewing it usually inspired
    A. disgust.   B. indifference.   C. awe.

5. When Jill accepted with alacrity the difficult task he gave her, her boss was
    A. annoyed.   B. impressed.   C. furious.

6. When Thoreau calls government an expedient, he means it is a
    A. tool.   B. useless enterprise.   C. bureaucracy.

7. People display magnanimity when they
    A. hold a grudge.   B. give to charity.   C. perform tasks efficiently.

8. Capture was evitable if the fugitive remained
    A. unknown.   B. hidden.   C. calm.

from **Walden** and *from* **Civil Disobedience** by Henry David Thoreau
Grammar and Style: Infinitives and Infinitive Phrases

An **infinitive** usually consists of the basic form of a verb preceded by the word *to*. It can function as a noun, an adjective, or an adverb.

Thoreau liked *to read*. [noun; object of verb *liked*]

Jo had several chapters *to read*. [adjective; modifies noun *chapters*]

Some people live *to read*. [adverb; modifies verb *live*]

An **infinitive phrase** consists of an infinitive and its complement and/or modifiers. The entire phrase serves as a noun, adjective, or adverb.

Thoreau liked *to read philosophy*. [noun; object of verb *liked*]

Jo had several chapters *to read quickly*. [adjective; modifies noun *chapters*]

Some people live *to read novels*. [adverb; modifies verb *live*]

A. PRACTICE: *For each sentence, underline the infinitive or infinitive phrase and indicate how it is functioning by writing* n *for noun,* adj *for adjective, or* adv *for adverb. Place the abbreviation on the line before the sentence.*

_____   1. I wished to live deliberately.

_____   2. I wanted to ponder only the essential facts of life.

_____   3. Perhaps it seemed to me that I had several more lives to live.

B. Writing Application: *Rewrite the following pairs of wordy sentences by turning one sentence into an infinitive phrase. You will need to change or delete some words.*

1. Thoreau wanted a certain kind of life. He was interested in living simply.

    _____

    _____

2. He follows the Transcendentalist teaching. That teaching stresses making a friend of nature.

    _____

    _____

3. Thoreau tells individuals some advice. He advises that they heed the sound of a different drummer.

    _____

    _____

Name _____ Date _____

from **Walden** and *from* **Civil Disobedience** by Henry David Thoreau
Support for Writing

As you prepare to write your editorial about the relevance of Thoreau's ideas today, reread the selections. Decide whether you support or reject Thoreau's ideas. Make entries into the chart below that strengthen your position.

Editorial on Simplicity
Why I Support or Reject Thoreau's Ideas of Simplicity: _____
Examples from today's world to support my opinion: _____   _____
Examples from Thoreau's world to support my opinion: _____   _____
Direct quotes from Thoreau that strengthen my position: _____   _____

On a separate page, write a draft of your editorial. Then revise it, and be sure to justify the choice you have made with examples from Thoreau or with examples from today's world. Submit your editorial to the school newspaper.

from **Walden** and *from* **Civil Disobedience** by Henry David Thoreau
Support for Extend Your Learning

Listening and Speaking

As you work with a small group to stage a **debate** about the pros and cons of civil disobedience as a form of social protest, keep the following in mind:

- Develop several key arguments supporting your position.
- Use familiar situations as examples that help listeners appreciate your points.
- Try to connect major and minor premises to strengthen your arguments.

Present your debate in pairs who present pro and con positions. Have listeners judge the persuasiveness of each debater's presentation.

Research and Technology

As you prepare an **oral presentation** on the state of Walden today, research the site on the Internet and enter material into the compare/contrast chart below.

Walden: Then and Now	
Walden in Thoreau's Time Description of Area	Walden Today Description of Area
Walden in Thoreau's Time Description of Cabin	Walden Today Description of Cabin
Walden in Thoreau's Time Who Lived Nearby	Walden Today Conservation Efforts

Present your findings to the class. Create a display, taking material from several reports, to show how Walden has been restored and how it is used by people.

Name _____ Date _____

from **Walden** and from **Civil Disobedience** by Henry David Thoreau
Enrichment: Social Studies

Authors of both nonfiction and fiction often respond to important contemporary events. Thoreau was especially concerned with two controversial issues of his day—slavery and the war between the United States and Mexico. He opposed both and even refused to pay taxes to a government that condoned them. His protest led to a night in jail—and to his famous essay on civil disobedience.

DIRECTIONS: *Following are some important events of Thoreau's day. Using your knowledge of his attitudes and writings, decide how Thoreau probably would have felt about each event. On the line before it, write S if you think he would have supported it and O if you think he would have opposed it. Explain why on the lines that follow. Support your answer with an example or detail from one of the selections.*

____ 1. Campaigning for the presidency in 1844, James K. Polk said it was the "manifest destiny" of the United States to expand its boundaries from Texas to the Pacific Ocean.

_____

_____

____ 2. In March of 1846, General Zachary Taylor moved American troops into the Mexican part of Texas.

_____

_____

____ 3. In May of 1846, the United States declared war on Mexico.

_____

_____

____ 4. A young American congressman named Abraham Lincoln challenged President Polk to prove that the land on which American troops were fighting was really American and not Mexican.

_____

_____

____ 5. In 1846, Congressman David Wilmot proposed that slavery should not be permitted in any territory that might be acquired from Mexico.

_____

_____

____ 6. In 1846, a great many people, from Ralph Waldo Emerson to Lieutenant Ulysses S. Grant, condemned the Mexican War as a "shameful theft."

_____

_____

Name _____ Date _____

from **Walden** and *from* **Civil Disobedience** by Henry David Thoreau
Selection Test A

Critical Reading *Identify the letter of the choice that best answers the question.*

____ 1. At the beginning of the selection from *Walden*, what does Thoreau allow himself to do through his imagination?
   A. build houses all over his town
   B. buy all the farms in his area
   C. make as much money as he can
   D. collect seeds from nearby places

____ 2. What part of Thoreau's philosophy is found in this passage from *Walden*?

   Our life is frittered away by details. An honest man has hardly need to count more than his ten fingers, or in extreme cases he may add his ten toes, and lump the rest.

   A. paying attention to details
   B. living a life of simplicity
   C. aiming for personal honesty
   D. working with one's hands

____ 3. What is a regular element of Thoreau's style in *Walden*?
   A. to ask questions and then answer them
   B. to state main ideas only once
   C. to jump quickly from idea to idea
   D. to expand on personal experiences

____ 4. Which element of Thoreau's style is shown in these passages from *Walden*?

   Simplicity, simplicity, simplicity! I say, let your affairs be as two or three, and not a hundred or a thousand . . . Simplify, simplify. Instead of three meals a day, if it be necessary eat but one; instead of a hundred dishes, five . . .

   A. using mathematical examples
   B. using themes from the kitchen
   C. repeating main ideas
   D. using only short sentences

____ 5. Which of Thoreau's main beliefs is expressed in this passage from *Walden*?

   If a man does not keep pace with his companions, perhaps it is because he hears a different drummer. Let him step to the music which hears, however measured or far away.

   A. a belief in appreciating music
   B. a belief in doing what others do
   C. a belief in living as an individual
   D. a belief in having close friends

____ 6. What situation caused Thoreau to write *Civil Disobedience*?
   A. trade laws with India
   B. uprisings in California
   C. the Mexican War
   D. President Polk's election

____ 7. What does Thoreau call for, in terms of government, at the conclusion of this selection from *Civil Disobedience*?
   A. a better government
   B. no government at all
   C. a government run by businesses
   D. a government run by a king

____ 8. What is Thoreau's central idea in *Civil Disobedience*?
   A. the ability of government to control others
   B. the importance of trade in government
   C. the ability of people to govern themselves
   D. the importance of armies in government

Vocabulary and Grammar

____ 9. In which of these sentences is the meaning of the word *superfluous* expressed?
   A. Thoreau imagined himself buying all the farms around his town.
   B. Thoreau wanted to get all unnecessary concerns out of his life.
   C. Thoreau believed governments were best when they governed not at all.
   D. Thoreau believed in the importance of individual action.

____ 10. Which of these phrases is an infinitive phrase?
   A. "I wished to live deliberately"
   B. "took his farm at his price"
   C. "let your affairs be as two or three"
   D. "The light which puts out our eyes"

Essay

11. In *Walden,* Thoreau says, "I left the woods for as good a reason as I went there. Perhaps it seemed to me that I had several more lives to live, and could not spare any more time for that one. It is remarkable how easily and insensibly we fall into a particular route, and make a beaten track for ourselves." What do you think he means by falling into "a particular route"? Why does he see doing the same thing over and over as a problem? Write a brief essay to express your opinions. Use at least two examples from *Walden* to support your opinions.

12. In *Civil Disobedience,* how does Thoreau compare governments to people, in terms of getting things done? Does he think governments are useful? Write a brief essay to express Thoreau's beliefs. Use at least two examples from *Civil Disobedience* to support your ideas.

Name _____ Date _____

from Walden and **from Civil Disobedience** by Henry David Thoreau
Selection Test B

Critical Reading *Identify the letter of the choice that best completes the statement or answers the question.*

_____ 1. Which of these statements best reflects Thoreau's philosophy as expressed in *Walden*?
   A. Human beings are creatures of great complexity.
   B. Building a cabin in the woods is practical and inexpensive.
   C. Wealth is desirable, but spiritual happiness is also important.
   D. Living a simple life close to nature lets a person concentrate on important things.

_____ 2. What aspect of his philosophy does Thoreau express in the following statement?
   If a man does not keep pace with his companions, perhaps it is because he hears a different drummer.
   A. love of nature
   B. individualism
   C. lack of materialism
   D. emphasis on simplicity

_____ 3. What is Thoreau's main point about time in the paragraph beginning "Time is but the stream I go a-fishing in"?
   A. Time is shallow, but eternity remains.
   B. Time is elusive; we cannot pin it down.
   C. To succeed in life, you must harness time and make it work for you.
   D. Time is of the essence.

_____ 4. One aspect of Thoreau's style is to
   A. begin a paragraph with a specific event and build to a general truth.
   B. avoid repetition of words or ideas.
   C. follow each long sentence with a short, punchy sentence.
   D. ask a series of rhetorical questions.

_____ 5. How does Thoreau's style reinforce his theme of living with deliberation?
   A. by relying on unusually difficult words
   B. by instructing the reader to pay attention
   C. by imitating a scientific report
   D. by repeating his main ideas

_____ 6. What does Thoreau hope to convey with the description of the path his feet had worn to the pondside within a week?
   A. Establishing habits makes daily living easier.
   B. Human beings fall into dull routines all too readily.
   C. Living far away from friends is good discipline.
   D. Everyone should march to the same tune.

____ 7. What message does Thoreau hope to convey with his anecdote of the strong and beautiful bug in the conclusion of *Walden*?

    A. Life can be beautiful, but it can also be dangerous.

    B. Not all bugs are ugly.

    C. Something that appears lifeless can give rise to new life.

    D. Carpenters live simple lives close to nature.

____ 8. *Walden*'s closing image of the morning star leaves readers feeling

    A. inspired.

    B. hopeless.

    C. exhausted.

    D. argumentative.

____ 9. What is the central idea of *Civil Disobedience*?

    A. People must overthrow the government.

    B. Trade and commerce should be strictly regulated.

    C. The fewer people who run the government, the better.

    D. Citizens should be willing to act on their opinions.

____ 10. In *Civil Disobedience*, how does Thoreau support his view that the government is abused by powerful individuals?

    A. He compares American and foreign governments.

    B. He analyzes the structure of America's government.

    C. He cites the examples of an unpopular war.

    D. He alludes to several corrupt Massachusetts politicians.

____ 11. Thoreau's view of the war with Mexico is best described as

    A. patriotic.

    B. indifferent.

    C. critical.

    D. practical.

____ 12. Which word best describes Thoreau's style in *Civil Disobedience*?

    A. objective

    B. repetitive

    C. scholarly

    D. casual

____ 13. Based on *Civil Disobedience*, what can you infer about Thoreau's political philosophy?

    A. He relies on government leaders for moral guidance.

    B. He feels it is America's destiny to spread to the Pacific Ocean.

    C. He stresses that we must all work together to accomplish great deeds.

    D. He believes that people are politically responsible for themselves.

_____ 14. How does *Civil Disobedience* reflect ideas of Transcendentalism?
    A. It stresses the individual's ability to judge the actions of government.
    B. It proposes looking at nature as a way to govern harmoniously.
    C. It implies that democratic governments, too, have an Over-Soul and are more spiritually attuned to people's needs than any one individual can ever be.
    D. It stresses that warfare is sometimes the only means by which oppression can be cast off and society changed.

Vocabulary and Grammar

_____ 15. What does Thoreau mean when he describes the fences as *dilapidated*?
    A. They are under construction.
    B. They need to be repaired.
    C. There are many fences.
    D. The fences are very high.

_____ 16. Which of these sentences contains an infinitive or an infinitive phrase used as a noun?
    A. Thoreau went to the woods.
    B. Thoreau wanted to live deliberately.
    C. By simplifying his life, Thoreau concentrated on important ideas.
    D. To simply his life, Thoreau concentrated on important ideas.

_____ 17. Which word below can substitute for the italicized word in this sentence?
    Thoreau thinks people spend too much time on *superfluous* concerns.
    A. upper-class
    B. unnatural
    C. unnecessary
    D. important

Essay

18. Based on *Walden,* what would you say that living in the woods taught Thoreau about the human spirit and the natural world? Answer this question in a short essay, and support your evaluation with details from the selection.

19. In both *Civil Disobedience* and *Walden,* Thoreau urges people to act. How would Thoreau define taking action? Does action imply physical activity? When does Thoreau think people should take action? What action does he think they should take? Using examples from the selection, write a short essay responding to these questions.

Vocabulary Warm-up Word Lists

Study these words from the selections. Then, complete the activities.

Word List A

absorb [ab SORB] *v.* to suck up; to take in and incorporate; to assimilate
It took us hours to <u>absorb</u> all the information from the lengthy chapter.

assignable [uh SYN uh buhl] *adj.* able to be given away
In her will, she left the <u>assignable</u> parts of her estate to her favorite niece.

keepsakes [KEEP sayks] *n.* souvenirs; mementoes; heirlooms
Mother has a trunk full of <u>keepsakes</u> in the attic.

leisure [LEE zhuhr] *n.* free time; relaxation
Timothy uses much of his <u>leisure</u> for reading.

onset [ON set] *n.* approach; beginning
A tickling in my throat signaled the <u>onset</u> of a cold.

portion [POR shuhn] *n.* part; section
The dessert was so large that I could eat only a <u>portion</u> of it.

quivering [KWIV uhr ing] *adj.* shivering
When the dog barked loudly, the cat retreated, <u>quivering</u> with fear.

wrung [RUNG] *v.* squeezed; compressed
I <u>wrung</u> out the shirt I had washed, squeezing all the water from it.

Word List B

befel [bee FEL] *v.* happened (modern spelling **befell**)
What fate <u>befell</u> the hero in that novel?

finite [FY nyt] *adj.* limited; able to be calculated or reckoned
Although the speed of light is unbelievably fast, it is still <u>finite</u>.

immortality [i mor TAL i tee] *n.* eternal life
The heroes of ancient epics often had <u>immortality</u> as their goal.

majority [muh JOR uh tee] *n.* greater part or larger number; more than half the total
The <u>majority</u> of voters did not agree with the governor, and he was not re-elected.

strove [STROHV] *v.* tried very hard; struggled
Each team <u>strove</u> hard for victory, but the outcome of the game was a tie score.

surmised [suhr MYZD] *v.* guessed; made an inference
From his remarks, we <u>surmised</u> that Keith was not in favor of our proposal.

unveil [un VAYL] *v.* to uncover; to reveal
The museum director planned to <u>unveil</u> a dramatic new painting.

valves [VALVZ] *n.* gates or devices regulating the flow of a liquid
The <u>valves</u> in that automobile engine need regular lubrication.

Name _____ Date _____

Poems by Emily Dickinson
Vocabulary Warm-up Exercises

Exercise A *Fill in the blanks, using each word from Word List A only once.*

Elaine had promised herself that, when she had a day of [1] _____, she

would do some gardening. All winter, she had tried to [2] _____

all the tips she could from gardening magazines. She had carefully charted

each [3] _____ of the ground, calculating what part was

[4] _____ to rose bushes and how much for vegetables and herbs.

On Saturday morning, she gathered her gardening tools, some of which were

[5] _____ left her by her grandmother. The weather was sunny and still:

not a leaf was shaking or [6] _____ on the trees. Elaine worked all day

long—digging, planting, and watering. With the [7] _____ of twilight, she

had the work done. She felt happy but [8] _____ out with fatigue.

Exercise B *Revise each sentence so that the underlined vocabulary word is logical. Be sure to keep the vocabulary word in your revision.*

Example: Because the work was so <u>arduous</u>, we completed it quickly and easily.
Because the work was so <u>arduous</u>, we had a hard time completing it.

1. Two setbacks <u>befell</u> James, and he was relieved to have avoided them.

   _____

2. Because our resources are <u>finite</u>, we can pledge any amount of money for that cause.

   _____

3. The <u>immortality</u> of the Greek gods was one way in which they resembled humans.

   _____

4. The election was close, and the loser received a very small <u>majority</u> of votes.

   _____

5. In all his undertakings, Tom <u>strove</u> hard, putting in minimum effort.

   _____

6. Unwilling to use an educated guess, Phil <u>surmised</u> the ending from hints in the story.

   _____

7. In favor of concealing the new painting, the museum director prepared to <u>unveil</u> it.

   _____

8. <u>Valves</u> are used to heat the water in those pipes.

   _____

Name _____ Date _____

Poems by Emily Dickinson
Reading Warm-up A

Read the following passage. Pay special attention to the underlined words. Then, read it again, and complete the activities. Use a separate sheet of paper for your written answers.

Cathy often finished her homework early. Most nights she had an hour or two of <u>leisure</u> before dinner. Sometimes she played with her baby sister Betsy or read stories to the little girl—usually fairy tales that left Betsy <u>quivering</u> with delight.

At other times Cathy would write in her journal. She always reserved a <u>portion</u> of each journal page for notes about subjects for poems. She would fill this section with ideas she had trained herself to <u>absorb</u> during the day, such as sensory images she'd accumulated on the school bus, in the cafeteria, or on the playing field. Cathy also got ideas for poems from short stories she read in English class. She felt that each fictional character she encountered in a story should be <u>assignable</u> to a poem. Perhaps she might use the character in a story poem. Maybe she would write a lyric poem using the character as the speaker.

Now that it was late fall, with the <u>onset</u> of winter not far off, Cathy wanted to increase the rate at which she wrote notes. During the winter, when the weather was bad, she would stay indoors upstairs at her little desk, depending on the notes to create poetry.

Cathy had heard from her mother that her grandmother, Hetty Pierce, had followed this same system. Some of Hetty's poems, scribbled on old envelopes and the back of shopping lists, had survived and were treasured in the family as <u>keepsakes</u>. These poems dated from the days of the Great Depression and World War II, a difficult time when Hetty had <u>wrung</u> beautiful verse out of the challenges of her life experience. Cathy felt as if she were following in Hetty's footsteps. She knew that poetry would always be a close companion, wherever her life might lead.

1. Underline the words in this sentence and the previous one that give a clue to the meaning of <u>leisure</u>. Use the word *leisure* in an original sentence.

2. Circle the words in this sentence that give a clue to the meaning of <u>quivering</u>. What is a synonym for *quivering*?

3. Underline the words in this sentence and the next that give a clue to the meaning of <u>portion</u>. What is a synonym for *portion*?

4. Circle the words that offer a clue to the meaning of <u>absorb</u> here. What are two synonyms for the word *absorb*?

5. Circle the words in this sentence and the next two sentences that offer clues to the meaning of <u>assignable</u>. What are a verb and a noun related to this adjective?

6. Underline the words in this sentence that give a clue to the meaning of <u>onset</u>. What are two synonyms for *onset*?

7. Circle the words in this sentence that give a clue to the meaning of <u>keepsakes</u>. Use the word *keepsakes* in an original sentence.

8. Underline the words in this sentence hinting at the meaning of <u>wrung</u>. What is a synonym for *wrung*?

Poems by Emily Dickinson
Reading Warm-up B

Read the following passage. Pay special attention to the underlined words. Then, read it again, and complete the activities. Use a separate sheet of paper for your written answers.

In her poetry, Emily Dickinson <u>strove</u> to create a distinctive style, and most readers will probably agree that she succeeded brilliantly in this effort. What is the hallmark of this style? In the <u>majority</u> of Dickinson's poems, it is the use of surprise. There are very few Dickinson poems that are entirely predictable.

Surprises in Dickinson come in a number of forms. By combining slant or approximate rhyme with exact rhyme, for example, she keeps the reader guessing about the sound of the poem. Another important Dickinson technique is sudden changes in rhythm. Try reading "Water, is taught by thirst" aloud, for example. If you think you have <u>surmised</u> or inferred how the poem ought to unfold, you may be surprised by the unexpected variations Dickinson uses to hold the reader's attention. Dickinson also uses surprising word choices, such as the noun *valves* in the next-to-last line of "The Soul selects her own Society." This word suggests mechanical devices, as if the soul had water spigots or faucets that could be turned on or off.

Dickinson also exploits surprises in the speaker's point of view. In several of her poems, for example, we learn that death <u>befell</u> the speaker before the poem opens. The emotions the speaker conveys are either linked to the moment of death, or they are given from the perspective of someone approaching the threshold of <u>immortality</u>.

Finally, Dickinson makes extensive use of paradoxes, or apparent contradictions. A good example is the phrase *finite infinity* at the close of "There is a solitude of space." How can unlimited space, time, or distance be <u>finite</u>, or limited? Surprising paradoxes such as this one often help to <u>unveil</u> or reveal Dickinson's keenly observant themes about human nature and behavior.

1. Underline the words in this sentence that give a clue to the meaning of <u>strove</u>. Use the word **strove** in an original sentence.

2. Circle the word in this sentence and the next that hint at the meaning of <u>majority</u>. Use a word meaning the opposite of **majority** in a sentence of your own.

3. Underline the words in this sentence hinting at the meaning of <u>surmised</u>. What is a synonym for **surmised**?

4. Underline the words in this sentence and the next that give a clue to the meaning of <u>valves</u>.

5. Circle the words in this sentence that give a clue to the meaning of <u>befell</u>. What is a synonym for **befell**?

6. Underline the words in this sentence that hint at the meaning of <u>immortality</u>. Use a word meaning the opposite of **immortality** in an original sentence.

7. Underline the words in this sentence that give a clue to the meaning of <u>finite</u>. What is a synonym for **finite**?

8. Circle the words in this sentence that hint at the meaning of the word <u>unveil</u>. What are two antonyms for **unveil**?

Name _____ Date _____

Emily Dickinson's Poetry
Literary Analysis: Slant Rhyme

In **exact rhyme,** two or more words have the identical vowel and final consonant sounds in their last stressed syllables. For example, *pound* and *sound* rhyme exactly, as do *brain* and *contain.* In **slant rhyme,** the final sounds are similar but not identical. For example, *pond* and *sound* are slant rhymes, as are *brain* and *frame*.

DIRECTIONS: *On the lines after each passage from Dickinson's poetry, identify the words that rhyme, and indicate whether the rhymes are exact or slant.*

1. My life closed twice before its close—
   It yet remains to see
   If Immortality unveil
   A third event to me.

   _____

   _____

2. Or rather—He passed Us—
   The Dews drew quivering and chill—
   For only Gossamer, my Gown—
   My Tippet—only Tulle—

   _____

   _____

3. None may teach it—Any—
   'Tis the Seal Despair—
   An imperial affliction
   Sent us of the Air—

   _____

   _____

4. Compared with that profounder site
   That polar privacy
   A soul admitted to itself—
   Finite Infinity.

   _____

   _____

Emily Dickinson's Poetry
Reading Strategy: Analyze Images

Good poets use language efficiently to create images that appeal to one or more of the five senses: sight, touch, hearing, taste, and smell. Often these concrete images help a poet convey abstract ideas. Consider the images in this stanza, which appeal to the senses of sight and touch:

> The Brain is deeper than the sea—
> For—hold them—Blue to Blue—
> The one the other will absorb—
> As Sponges—Buckets—do—

The brain, says Dickinson, is like a wide blue sea, only deeper—so deep, in fact, that it absorbs the sea as easily as a sponge absorbs a bucketful of water. The image of the wide blue sea helps us visualize the brain. The image of the sponge absorbing the bucketful of water helps us visualize the brain's activity and appreciate its capacity.

DIRECTIONS: *On the lines after each stanza from "The Soul selects her own Society—," explain how the image or images that the stanza contains help to convey abstract ideas.*

1. The Soul selects her own Society—
   Then—shuts the door—
   To her divine Majority—
   Present no more—

   _____

   _____

   _____

   _____

   _____

2. Unmoved—she notes the Chariots—pausing—
   At her low Gate—
   Unmoved—an Emperor be kneeling
   Upon her Mat—

   _____

   _____

   _____

   _____

   _____

Emily Dickinson's Poetry
Vocabulary Builder

Using the Root *-finis-*

A. DIRECTIONS: *The root -finis-, often shortened to -fin-, means "end" or "limit." On the lines provided, explain how the meaning of the word is conveyed in each of the following words.*

1. define _____

_____

2. refinish _____

_____

3. finale _____

_____

Using the Word List

cornice	surmised	oppresses	finite	infinity

B. DIRECTIONS: *On the line provided, write the word from the Word List that best completes each sentence.*

1. From her expression, I _____ that she was not happy to see me.
2. There had to be an end to the tunnel, but it seemed to stretch into _____.
3. Whenever a sad thought _____ me, I get a headache.
4. Only a _____ number of ways existed to solve the problem.
5. The skyscraper's northwest _____ was too high to see from the ground.

C. DIRECTIONS: *On the line, write the letter of the pair of words that expresses a relationship most like the pair in capital letters.*

___ 1. FINITE : INFINITY ::
    A. fatal : fate
    B. endless : eternity
    C. mortal : immortality
    D. significant : importance

___ 2. CORNICE : HOUSE ::
    A. pizza : pepperoni
    B. sweep : broom
    C. flue : chimney
    D. hat : head

___ 3. SURMISED : SPECULATION ::
    A. anticipated : compliment
    B. forewarned : prediction
    C. flattered : insult
    D. pampered : aid

___ 4. OPPRESSED : CAREFREE ::
    A. thoughtful : serious
    B. grumpy : cheerful
    C. ancient : old
    D. depressed : sad

Name _____ Date _____

Grammar and Style: Gerunds

Gerunds are verb forms that end in *-ing* but are used as nouns, functioning as subjects, direct objects, predicate nominatives, or objects of prepositions.

Gerund as subject:	*Socializing* was difficult for Dickinson.
Gerund as direct object:	She avoided *socializing*.
Gerund as predicate nominative:	Perhaps her least favorite task was *socializing*.
Gerund as object of a preposition:	She disliked the small talk of *socializing*.

A. PRACTICE: *Circle the gerunds in the following sentences. On the line before each sentence, write S if the gerund is used as a subject, DO if it is used as the direct object of a verb, PA if it is used as a predicate nominative, or OP if it is used as the object of a preposition.*

____ 1. Talking about politics always made Mario's grandmother angry.

____ 2. Alex dreamed about dancing with the Joffrey Ballet.

____ 3. When it comes to sports, Germaine prefers swimming.

____ 4. My favorite sport is running.

____ 5. Grandfather is famous for his cooking.

B. Writing Application: *On the lines provided, write a sentence using each word as a gerund. In the eight sentences you write in total, try to illustrate all four gerund uses: subject, direct object, predicate nominative, and object of a preposition.*

1. jumping _____

_____

2. asking _____

_____

3. participating _____

_____

4. debating _____

_____

5. signaling _____

_____

Emily Dickinson's Poetry
Support for Writing

As you plan to write a letter to Emily Dickinson about her poetry, choose one poem as a focus. Organize your thoughts by filling in the chart below.

Letter to Emily Dickinson	
Title of Dickinson Poem	
Main ideas I liked	
Main images I liked	
New understanding I have gained from your poetry	

On a separate page, write a draft of your letter. Be sure to use the correct forms of salutation and closing. Develop each of your ideas from the chart in a separate paragraph. As you revise your letter, be sure you make clear transitions from one paragraph to another. Remember to thank Dickinson for her wonderful poetry.

Emily Dickinson's Poetry
Support for Extend Your Learning

Listening and Speaking

After you've chosen three of Emily Dickinson's poems to read in a class **poetry reading,** rehearse the poems to yourself. Follow these guidelines as you read:

- Follow punctuation—including dashes—for pauses.
- Speak clearly, letting the poem's meaning show in your emphasis.

After you have read your poems, ask your classmates for feedback. What are their reactions to listening to poetry read aloud, as opposed to reading it in a book?

Research and Technology

As you prepare a **report** about the relationship of Emily and her brother Austin, do research in library biographies and on the Internet. Enter your findings in the biography table below.

Emily and Austin: Sister and Brother
Emily/Birth and Death Dates Experiences with Brother/Brother in Poems
Austin/Birth and Death Dates Experiences with Sister/Opinions about Sister's Poems

On a separate page, write a report about the relationship between the brother and sister. Combine your report with a selection of Dickinson's poems and present your report to the class.

Emily Dickinson's Poetry
Enrichment: Art

Poets often explore the same topics and themes in several different poems. Emily Dickinson frequently returns to topics such as nature, solitude, and death. Consequently, some of the images that she found most striking appear in more than one poem. Each time the image is approached from a different angle, or used in a different way. In the poems in your text, Dickinson writes about solitude several times. Here are two examples.

There is a solitude of space
A solitude of sea
A solitude of death, but these
Society shall be
Compared with that profounder site
That polar privacy
A soul admitted to itself—
Finite Infinity.

The Soul selects her own Society—
Then—shuts the Door—
To her divine Majority—
Present no more—. . .

In the first selection, Dickinson writes about solitude as if it were the same as limitless empty space. In the second selection, though, she writes about solitude as if it meant being trapped in a limited space, behind a door. The painting that accompanies the first poem could not illustrate the second, but it could illustrate other poems that mention empty, sweeping spaces.

DIRECTIONS: *Four of the poems by Emily Dickinson in your textbook are accompanied by paintings. Choose two of these paintings. Explain how each painting illustrates an image in the poem it accompanies. Then consider whether these paintings could be used to illustrate other images in other poems by Emily Dickinson. Write the name of one other poem that each painting might illustrate, and explain how this painting relates to messages and themes that appear throughout Dickinson's work. Use the space below to organize your work.*

1. Name of painting: _____

   Poem it illustrates: _____

   Image the picture illustrates: _____

   Another poem the painting could illustrate: _____

   How the painting relates to Dickinson's messages and themes: _____

   _____

   _____

2. Name of painting: _____

   Poem it illustrates: _____

   Image the picture illustrates: _____

   Another poem the painting could illustrate: _____

   How the painting relates to Dickinson's messages and themes: _____

   _____

   _____

Emily Dickinson's Poetry
Selection Test A

Critical Reading *Identify the letter of the choice that best answers the question.*

_____ 1. Who are some of the important characters in the carriage in "Because I could not stop for Death—"?
   I.   Death
   II. the speaker
   III. Children
   IV. A man
   A. I and III
   B. II and IV
   C. I and IV
   D. I and II

_____ 2. In "Because I could not stop for Death—", what image does the poet use to represent Death?
   A. an undertaker in a graveyard
   B. a teacher at a children's school
   C. a kind, polite gentleman
   D. a fast-driving carriage owner

_____ 3. In the following stanza from "I heard a Fly buzz—when I died—," which words form a slant rhyme?
   The Eyes around—had wrung them dry— / And Breaths were gathering firm / For that last Onset—when the King / Be witnessed—in the Room—
   A. *dry* and *firm*
   B. *King* and *Room*
   C. *dry* and *King*
   D. *firm* and *Room*

_____ 4. Which stage of life does the image of late-afternoon winter light represent in "There's a certain Slant of light,"?
   A. when a person is newly born
   B. when a person thinks of death
   C. when a person becomes an adult
   D. when a person thinks of family

_____ 5. In the following stanza from "The Soul selects it own Society," which pair of words forms a slant rhyme?

> Unmoved—she notes the Chariots—pausing— / At her low Gate— / Unmoved—an Emperor be kneeling / Upon her Mat—

    A. *pausing* and *Gate*
    B. *pausing* and *Mat*
    C. *Gate* and *Mat*
    D. *Gate* and *kneeling*

_____ 6. Which two images does the poet link to show the human ability to absorb and hold its experience in "The Brain—is wider than the Sky—"?

    A. the Brain and the Sky
    B. the Brain and the Sea
    C. the Brain and a Sponge
    D. the Brain and God

_____ 7. In the following stanza from "The Brain—is wider than the Sky—," which words create an exact rhyme?

> The Brain is deeper than the sea— / For—hold them—Blue to Blue— / The one the other will absorb— / As Sponges—Buckets—do—

    A. *sea* and *Blue*
    B. *Blue* and *absorb*
    C. *Blue* and *do*
    D. *absorb* and *do*

_____ 8. What is the message of the poem "Water, is taught by thirst."?

    A. Opposites teach about each other.
    B. Thirsty people long for water.
    C. Life has difficult challenges.
    D. Battles and war are unnecessary.

Vocabulary and Grammar

_____ 9. In which sentence is the meaning of the word *oppresses* expressed?

    A. The poet writes about how the death of loved ones weighs on her.
    B. She composes several poems about the nature of death.
    C. The poet has a rich imagination that shows in her poetry.
    D. Though she has few visitors, she is close to her family.

___ **10.** Which of the following passages from Emily Dickinson's poetry contains a word ending in *-ing* used as a subject?

    A. "Parting is all we know of heaven."

    B. "We passed the fields of Gazing Grain—"

    C. "We passed the Setting Sun—"

    D. "Unmoved—an Emperor be kneeling"

Essay

11. In Dickinson's poem "Because I could not stop for Death—," she writes "For only Gossamer, my Gown— / My Tippet—only Tulle—." What do you think she is suggesting by writing of a woman going to her death and yet being dressed up in fine fabrics, such as gossamer and tulle? Why does she choose such an unexpected image? Write a brief essay to explain your opinion. Use examples from Emily Dickinson's poetry to support your opinion.

12. The poem "Water, is taught by thirst," uses pairs of images to show that opposites teach about each other. What other examples could you use to show the value of opposites? Think about the image pairs used in the poem: water and thirst, land and oceans, or peace and battles. Think about how we could not appreciate certain experiences without going through opposite experiences. Write a brief poem using some of the following pairs, as well as those of your own choosing:

food and hunger
sleep and wakefulness
sorrow and joy
night and sunrise

Emily Dickinson's Poetry
Selection Test B

Critical Reading *Identify the letter of the choice that best completes the statement or answers the question.*

____ 1. In "I heard a Fly buzz—when I died—," why is there a stillness in the room?
   A. The people in the room have stopped talking in order to listen to the fly.
   B. The people in the room are waiting for the speaker to make her will.
   C. The people in the room are waiting for the speaker's final moment.
   D. The storm outdoors has momentarily ceased its "heaves."

____ 2. In the following stanza from "I heard a Fly buzz—when I died—," which words create slant rhyme?
   I heard a Fly buzz—when I died— / The Stillness in the Room / Was like the Stillness in the Air— / Between the Heaves of Storm—
   A. *Air* and *Storm*
   B. *Room* and *Storm*
   C. *died* and *Room*
   D. *died* and *Air*

____ 3. Which of the following images is the central image in "Because I could not stop for Death—"?
   A. a carriage ride
   B. the horses' heads
   C. children playing
   D. the setting sun

____ 4. In "Because I could not stop for Death—," Death is personified as
   A. a polite gentleman.
   B. a rough and harried carriage driver.
   C. a weary gravedigger.
   D. a well-informed tour guide.

____ 5. Which of these statements best expresses the central message of "My life closed twice before its close—"?
   A. Our lives are divided into three parts, and death is the last one.
   B. Parting is heavenly when you are glad to be rid of someone but hellish when you know you will miss the person.
   C. Parting may be the closest we come in life to understanding death.
   D. Death is followed by immortality.

____ 6. What is the chief effect of the slant rhyme in this final stanza from "The Soul selects her own Society—"?
   I've known her—from an ample nation— / Choose One— / Then—close the Valves of her attention— / Like Stone—
   A. It creates a harmony that stresses how well the speaker knows the soul.
   B. It creates a disharmony that suggests strife in the ample nation.
   C. It creates a disharmony that echoes the unsociable actions of the soul.
   D. It captures the sound of the running water that the valves imply.

___ 7. Which of these sentences best summarizes "There's a certain Slant of light"?
A. An afternoon church service depresses the speaker.
B. The speaker expresses a wish to die.
C. A winter day reminds the speaker of her mortality.
D. The speaker is too depressed to go outside.

___ 8. To which senses do the images in the stanza appeal?

There's a certain Slant of light, / Winter Afternoons— / That oppresses, like the Heft / Of Cathedral Tunes—

A. sight, sound, and touch
B. sight, sound, and smell
C. sight, smell, and taste
D. sound, smell, and touch

___ 9. Which statement best paraphrases the central comparison in "There is a solitude of space"?
A. Compared to the solitude of death, the solitude of space and sea are like society.
B. Compared to the solitude of a soul admitted to itself, the solitude of space, sea, and death are like society.
C. Compared to the solitude of space, sea, and death, living in society is a more restrictive form of solitude.
D. Compared to the solitude of space and sea, the solitude of death is more profound.

___ 10. "The Brain—is wider than the Sky—" compares the physical size of the brain to that of the sky and the sea. What point is Dickinson making when she uses these images?
A. The brain is blue, like the sky and the sea.
B. The brain is infinitely large in understanding.
C. The brain is an empty space.
D. The human brain is physically larger than any other animal's.

___ 11. In these lines from "Water, is taught by thirst," which words provide slant rhyme?

Water, is taught by thirst. / Land—by the Oceans passed. / Transport—by throe— / Peace— by its battles told— / Love, by Memorial Mold— / Birds, by the Snow.

A. *thirst* and *passed*
B. *throe* and *told*
C. *told* and *Mold*
D. *throe* and *Snow*

___ 12. In "Water, is taught by thirst," the final image of the birds being taught by the snow most likely refers to
A. birds finding water to drink by melting the snow.
B. hawks and other birds of prey following tracks of small animals in the snow.
C. birds suffering when it snows because it is hard for them to find food.
D. birds learning to take bird baths in the snow.

_____ 13. Which of the following poems focuses most strongly on a lesson that can be learned from nature?
  A. "There is a solitude of space"
  B. "Because I could not stop for Death—"
  C. "My life closed twice before its close—"
  D. "There's a certain Slant of light"

Vocabulary and Grammar

_____ 14. Which word below is the best replacement for *surmised* in the lines "I first *surmised* the Horses Heads / Were toward Eternity—"?
  A. guessed
  B. screamed
  C. taught
  D. whispered

_____ 15. Where would you most likely see a *cornice*?
  A. on a tulle gown
  B. on a building
  C. on a carriage
  D. on a gravestone

_____ 16. Which of these sentences uses a gerund as a predicate nominative?
  A. Anna goes horseback riding every morning.
  B. Sometimes waiting can seem intolerable.
  C. Jarvis preferred to learn by listening.
  D. It was losing that made Antoine angry.

_____ 17. How is the gerund used in the following sentence?
    Rushing through the hall, Meena feared being late to class.

  A. as the subject of the sentence
  B. as the direct object of a verb
  C. as a predicate nominative
  D. as the object of a preposition

Essay

18. Consider the three Dickinson poems in your text that focus most on the subject of death: "I heard a Fly buzz—when I died—," "Because I could not stop for Death—," and "My life closed twice before its close—." Do you think Dickinson feared death? Why or why not? Write an essay explaining your answer.

19. Write an essay exploring the identity of the teachers and the lessons being taught in "Water, is taught by thirst." First, identify and compare the "teachers" in the poem. Then analyze the relationship between each teacher and the lesson taught, and determine what makes the relationships analogous to each other. Finally, discuss what you feel is the central message of the poem.

Poems by Walt Whitman
Vocabulary Warm-up Word Lists

Study these words from the selections. Then, complete the activities.

Word List A

applause [uh PLAWZ] *n.* approval or praise, shown by clapping hands
The audience burst out into loud <u>applause</u> at the end of the play.

astronomer [uh STRAHN uh muhr] *n.* scientist who studies the heavenly bodies
The <u>astronomer</u>'s specialty was the study of comets.

intermission [in ter MISH uhn] *n.* pause
Between the play's two acts there was a 15-minute <u>intermission</u>.

lectured [LEK chuhrd] *v.* delivered a talk or analysis in public
Professor Robinson <u>lectured</u> every Thursday morning to his economics class.

measureless [MEZH uhr luhs] *adj.* without measure or number; infinite
Before Columbus crossed the Atlantic, the ocean must have seemed <u>measureless</u>.

mechanics [muh KAN iks] *n.* workers skilled in using tools
Work on the space shuttle requires highly skilled, specialized <u>mechanics</u>.

moist [MOYST] *adj.* slightly wet; damp
The cushions on the patio were <u>moist</u> this morning from last night's rain.

venturing [VEN churh ing] *adj.* undertaking a risk
The explorers were <u>venturing</u> into unknown territory.

Word List B

abeyance [uh BAY uhns] *n.* temporary suspension
Our vacation plans are in <u>abeyance</u> due to the airline strike.

filament [FIL uh muhnt] *n.* very slender thread or fiber
The <u>filament</u> generated by the spider shimmered in the early-morning sunlight.

gossamer [GOS uh muhr] *adj.* made of very thin, soft, filmy cloth
The bride wore a <u>gossamer</u> veil, and her face could be seen clearly behind it.

isolated [Y suh layt uhd] *adj.* solitary; alone
The air force base was located on an <u>isolated</u> island that had few visitors.

melodious [muh LOH dee uhs] *adj.* tuneful
At the beginning of the musical, the orchestra struck up a <u>melodious</u> tune.

promontory [PRAHM uhn tor ee] *n.* crag; rocky outcropping
On the dramatic <u>promontory</u> of the cliff, an eagle stood, surveying the ocean.

unaccountable [un uh KOUNT uh buhl] *adj.* not able to be explained; strange
Hugo was <u>unaccountable</u> for his actions.

vacant [VAY kuhnt] *adj.* empty
The apartment building was <u>vacant</u>, awaiting demolition.

Poems by Walt Whitman
Vocabulary Warm-up Exercises

Exercise A *Fill in the blanks, using each word from Word List A only once.*

Dr. Conway taught one of the core science courses in the continuing education program for adults at the state college. A noted [1] _____, he had discovered several comets, and one was even named after him. He realized that many of his students were [2] _____ into scientific subjects for the first time. Some of them, in fact, were auto [3] _____, working for credits toward a college degree. Many of them were probably so nervous that their palms were [4] _____. So, when he [5] _____, Dr. Conway was careful to keep his delivery simple and clear. He often paused for a(n) [6] _____, to see if any of his points were unclear. His patience with the students was [7] _____. For their part, they appreciated his help and concern, and more than one of his lectures ended with [8] _____.

Exercise B *Decide whether each statement below is true or false. Circle T or F, and explain your answer.*

1. If you hold a project in *abeyance*, you suspend it temporarily.
   T / F _____

2. A *filament* is a thick strand of fiber.
   T / F _____

3. A garment made of *gossamer* cloth might be transparent.
   T / F _____

4. If people feel *isolated*, they may experience loneliness and sadness.
   T / F _____

5. A *melodious* tune appeals because it can be easily hummed or sung.
   T / F _____

6. A *promontory* may be located by digging deep down into the earth.
   T / F _____

7. If an explanation is *unaccountable*, it is logical and credible.
   T / F _____

8. If none of the motel rooms are *vacant*, it will not be possible to make a reservation.
   T / F _____

Poems by Walt Whitman
Reading Warm-up A

Read the following passage. Pay special attention to the underlined words. Then, read it again, and complete the activities. Use a separate sheet of paper for your written answers.

Sam stayed in his bedroom all afternoon, practicing for a poetry recitation at school. His teacher had assigned him Whitman's poem "When I Heard the Learn'd Astronomer." The more Sam recited the poem, the more he liked it. Still, he knew that poetry recitals were often boring, and he felt he would be nervous, <u>venturing</u> onto a stage with just a poem to keep everyone's attention.

To make matters worse, he kept imagining the situation described in the poem itself. He was the somber <u>astronomer</u> explaining the movements of the planets and stars with a series of charts. Instead of a wonder or mystery, the night sky became like the inside of a car engine, a bunch of objects to be tinkered with by <u>mechanics</u>. As he recited the poem, Sam could feel the atmosphere in the auditorium: the dim light, the air made <u>moist</u> by the breath of a few hundred people. He imagined just sitting there, unable to voice an opinion, as the astronomer <u>lectured</u> the crowd.

Wouldn't everyone feel just as bored tomorrow when Sam gave his reading? He imagined himself onstage, yelling out the words, while his fellow students yawned and waited for <u>intermission</u>, when they could leave the auditorium for a few minutes of fresh air. When he came to the end, they might clap a little, but the <u>applause</u> would be insincere.

How could he get across the real point of the poem, which was that the world and everything in it was fascinating? Inside a school auditorium, would anyone really be able to picture the night sky that the poem described, its mystery and its <u>measureless</u> size?

Probably not, Sam guessed, but when he looked at the poem again, he still liked it. All he could do was let it speak for itself.

1. Underline the word in this sentence that gives a clue to the meaning of <u>venturing</u>. Use the word **venturing** in a sentence of your own.

2. Circle the words in this sentence that give a clue to the meaning of <u>astronomer</u>. What is an adjective related to this word?

3. Underline the words that give a clue to the meaning of <u>mechanics</u>. Use this word in an original sentence.

4. Circle the words that offer a clue to the meaning of <u>moist</u> here. Use a word meaning the opposite of **moist** in a sentence of your own.

5. Circle the words in this sentence that offer clues to the meaning of <u>lectured</u>. What is a synonym of **lectured**?

6. Underline the words in this sentence that give a clue to the meaning of <u>intermission</u>. What are two synonyms for **intermission**?

7. Circle the words in this sentence that give a clue to the meaning of <u>applause</u>. Use the word **applause** in an original sentence.

8. Underline the words in this sentence hinting at the meaning of <u>measureless</u>. What are two synonyms for **measureless**?

Poems by Walt Whitman
Reading Warm-up B

Read the following passage. Pay special attention to the underlined words. Then, read it again, and complete the activities. Use a separate sheet of paper for your written answers.

Walt Whitman published his landmark work *Leaves of Grass* in 1855. For this poet, however, no work was ever really finished; it was held in <u>abeyance</u>, subject to periodic revision. For nearly forty years, Whitman brought out successive editions of *Leaves of Grass*, and the book became like a <u>filament</u>, a long and winding thread that recorded the poet's stages of development.

Work on *Leaves of Grass* did not leave Whitman <u>isolated</u>, focusing only on one priority. Whitman engaged his numerous talents in many different fields. In late 1862, for example, he heard that his younger brother George had been wounded at the Battle of Antietam; to be near him, Whitman traveled to a Washington hospital.

Civil War hospitals were scenes of <u>unaccountable</u> chaos, confusion, and misery. According to one officer, the Civil War was fought "at the end of the medical middle ages." Knowledge about sanitation, proper nutrition, and the causes of infection was <u>gossamer</u>-thin. Two thousand wounded men a day were pouring into Washington hospitals, and the beds in them were never <u>vacant</u>.

Whitman was so shocked by conditions that he decided to move to Washington to become a hospital volunteer, and for the next two years, he devoted his life to supporting the wounded men. He talked to the soldiers about their battle experiences; indeed, perhaps one of Whitman's most valuable services was as a listener to these lonely, suffering soldiers.

Somehow, Whitman found the inspiration to create <u>melodious</u> verse out of his hospital work in the poetry collection *Drum-Taps*, published in 1865. Although he had maintained that "the real war will never get in the books," his Civil War poems reveal him as a prophet or seer. He sits on a <u>promontory</u> or rocky outcropping, surveying the battlefields and revealing their glory and terror in a realistic, memorable vision.

1. Underline the words in this sentence that give a clue to the meaning of <u>abeyance</u>. Use the word **abeyance** in an original sentence.

2. Circle the words in this sentence that give a clue to the meaning of <u>filament</u>. Briefly explain the simile the writer uses in this sentence.

3. Underline the words in this sentence hinting at the meaning of <u>isolated</u>. What are two synonyms for the word *isolated*?

4. Underline the words in this sentence that give a clue to the meaning of <u>unaccountable</u>. What is an antonym for this word?

5. Circle the words in this and the previous sentence that give a clue to the meaning of <u>gossamer</u>. Is this word used literally or figuratively here?

6. Underline the words in this sentence that hint at the meaning of <u>vacant</u>. Use a word meaning the opposite of **vacant** in a sentence of your own.

7. Underline the words in this sentence that give a clue to the meaning of <u>melodious</u>. What is a synonym for *melodious*?

8. Circle the words in this sentence that hint at the meaning of the word <u>promontory</u>.

Walt Whitman's Poetry
Literary Analysis: Free Verse

Free verse is poetry with no fixed pattern of rhythm or line length. Instead, its rhythm captures the sound of natural speech, and its line lengths are determined solely by the content of the lines, with the poet breaking a line where there is a natural pause or where he or she wants a particular word or image emphasized. Whitman was a nineteenth-century pioneer of free verse, which he used in part to reflect his belief in individuality, democracy, and freedom.

DIRECTIONS: *The following stanza from "A Noiseless Patient Spider" has been rewritten using a fixed rhythmic pattern, or meter. On the lines below the two versions, comment on the differences between them.*

Whitman's version:

A noiseless patient spider,
I'd mark'd where on a little promontory it stood isolated,
Mark'd how to explore the vacant vast surrounding,
It launch'd forth filament, filament, filament, out of itself,
Ever unreeling them, ever tirelessly speeding them.

Metrical version:

A noiseless patient spider;
I marked the spot it stood on.
Alone on a high mountain,
It launched its silk lines forward,
Exploring its surroundings.

_____

_____

_____

_____

_____

_____

_____

_____

_____

_____

Name _____ Date _____

Walt Whitman's Poetry
Reading Strategy: Infer the Poet's Attitude

By examining a writer's choice of words and details, you can make inferences about the writer's attitude and gain insight into his or her feelings and beliefs. For example, in "When I Heard the Learn'd Astronomer," the words "tired" and "sick" suggest that Whitman has a negative attitude toward the astronomer and toward science in general, while the phrase "mystical, moist night air" and the detail about looking up "in perfect silence" at the stars suggest that Whitman has a positive attitude toward the nighttime sky and a more poetic approach toward viewing it.

DIRECTIONS: *Read each of these passages from "Song of Myself." Then circle the letter of the statement that comes closest to the attitude or world view that Whitman expresses in the passage.*

1. I loaf and invite my soul,
   I lean and loaf at my ease observing a spear of summer grass.
   A. People should not interfere with nature.
   B. Observation of nature is a valuable activity.
   C. Only lazy people have time to enjoy nature.

2. I, now thirty-seven years old in perfect health begin,
   Hoping to cease not till death.
   A. Life is an active business, not a passive one.
   B. Good health is essential to leading a good life.
   C. As one grows older, one naturally slows down.

3. The wild gander leads his flock through the cool night,
   Ya-honk he says, and sounds it down to me like an invitation.
   A. Wild creatures can inspire a sense of adventure in people.
   B. People are essentially followers, looking for a strong leader.
   C. Birds are unpleasant creatures that send secret messages few humans understand.

4. These are really the thoughts of all men in all ages and lands, they are not original with me,
   / If they are not yours as much they are mine they are nothing, or next to nothing.
   A. Any individual's voice is a humble voice, prone to error.
   B. The human soul is essentially the same in every time and place.
   C. If poetry does not express new ideas and feelings, it is worthless.

5. Do I contradict myself? / Very well then I contradict myself, / (I am large, I contain multitudes.)
   A. People who contradict themselves are phony hypocrites.
   B. To feel shame for being overweight is a foolish contradiction.
   C. The human spirit is capable of contradiction, which is no bad thing.

Walt Whitman's Poetry
Vocabulary Builder

Using the Root -fus-

A. DIRECTIONS: *The root -fus- means "pour." Keep that in mind as you write on the line the letter of the choice that best completes the following sentences.*

1. If Stella is perspiring *profusely*, she is probably sweating _____.
   A. a bit
   B. a lot
   C. due to illness
   D. during sleep

2. During a blood *transfusion*, blood _____.
   A. congeals
   B. turns blue
   C. cannot reach the heart
   D. goes from one person to another

3. If the sky at sunset is *suffused* with red, it _____.
   A. is filled with red
   B. contains very little red
   C. clashes with red
   D. has no red in it whatsoever

4. _____ might cause two pieces of metal to fuse together.
   A. High heat
   B. High cost
   C. Thickness
   D. Moisture

Using the Word List

abeyance	effuse

B. DIRECTIONS: *On the lines provided, rewrite each sentence by replacing the italicized word with a simpler word that means the same thing.*

1. I depart as air, I shake my white locks at the runaway sun, I *effuse* my flesh in eddies, and drift it in lacy jags.

   _____

2. Creeds and school in *abeyance*, retiring back a while suffced at what they are, but never forgotten.

   _____

C. DIRECTIONS: *On the line, write the letter of the word that is most nearly opposite in meaning to the word in capital letters.*

____ 1. ABEYANCE :
   A. suspension
   B. continuation
   C. vacation
   D. legality

____ 2. EFFUSE :
   A. pour
   B. appear
   C. contract
   D. boil

Walt Whitman's Poetry

Grammar and Style: Pronoun-Antecedent Agreement

A pronoun must agree in number and gender with its **antecedent,** the word to which it refers.

Singular masculine pronoun and antecedent:	The *boatman* sings as *he* sails *his* boat.
Singular feminine pronoun and antecedent:	The young *wife* sings as *she* does *her* work.
Singular neuter pronoun and antecedent:	The *spider* reached a high promontory where *it* made *its* web.
Plural pronoun and antecedent:	I heard many *astronomers,* and *they* all brought *their* charts with *them.*

A. PRACTICE: *Circle the pronoun in parentheses that correctly completes each sentence, and underline the antecedent to which the pronoun refers.*

1. Mrs. Pell likes poetry, and (his, her, its) favorite poet is Walt Whitman.

2. Mrs. Pell's volume of Whitman's poems has (its, her, their) cover damaged.

3. Two pictures of Whitman in (his, her, their) hat appear on the cover.

4. The book is published by a company in Boston; (it, he, they) also published Whitman's original volumes of verse in the late nineteenth century.

B. Writing Application: *On the lines provided, rewrite these sentences by replacing each italicized term with a pronoun that agrees with its antecedent in number and gender.*

1. Whitman leans and loafs at *Whitman's* ease, observing a spear of summer grass.

_____

2. Whitman notes that *Whitman's* ancestors include *Whitman's* parents and *Whitman's parents'* parents.

_____

3. When Whitman listened to the lecture, *Whitman* became tired and sick from looking at the charts and diagrams and measuring *the charts and diagrams.*

_____

4. Whitman's noiseless, patient spider explores a large area, and *the spider* spins filaments out of *the spider's* body, tirelessly unreeling *the filaments.*

_____

Walt Whitman's Poetry
Support for Writing

To organize your material to write a Whitman-esque poem (a poem in Whitman's style), enter details, language, and images in the chart below.

Poem in Imitation of Walt Whitman

Poem Subject/Title	
images	
arrangement of lines	
informal language/ examples of phrases	

On a separate page, write a draft of your poem. When you revise, be sure you have used a variety of line lengths, informal language and phrases, and lots of enthusiasm.

Walt Whitman's Poetry
Support for Extend Your Learning

Listening and Speaking

As you find photos of America today for a **collage,** try to imagine how some of the same scenes would have looked in Whitman's time. While you work on deciding how to present your collage to the class, consider the following:

- Explain why you included each image.
- Discuss how the themes of the collage compare to Whitman's vision of the country.

Choose some passages of Whitman's poetry to read as you present your collage to your classmates.

Research and Technology

As you listen to the poetry of Emily Dickinson and Walt Whitman on the Internet or on library CDs, compare them by entering material in the chart below.

Poetic Elements in Dickinson and Whitman

Emily Dickinson	Walt Whitman
Poetry Techniques _____ _____	Poetry Techniques _____ _____
Examples _____ _____	Examples _____ _____
Effect of Techniques _____ _____	Effect of Techniques _____ _____
Why this person is an important American poet _____ _____	Why this person is an important American poet _____ _____

On a separate page, write a short comparison of the two poets. Present your **report** to the class.

Walt Whitman's Poetry
Enrichment: Science

Scientists collect knowledge about the world in a careful and systematic way. They use the scientific method, which includes collecting data through observations and experiments, formulating and testing hypotheses, and drawing conclusions. Scientists strive to be objective in their work, trying not to be influenced by their personal beliefs, opinions, and emotions.

Poets, on the other hand, often do not approach the world in a scientific way. Poetry is usually written from a particular, subjective point of view. Poets usually do not do controlled experiments, although they may make observations and draw conclusions. The conclusions that poets draw, however, are different from scientific conclusions, since a poet's conclusions often are philosophical and/or emotional.

Consider Walt Whitman's poetry. Is Whitman more a scientist or a poet? Why do you think so?

DIRECTIONS: *Refer to Whitman's poems "When I Heard the Learn'd Astronomer" and "A Noiseless Patient Spider" to answer the questions below.*

1. What phrases in these poems show that Whitman approaches the stars and the spider more as a poet than as a scientist?

   _____

   _____

2. Does Whitman's approach to the natural world have anything in common with that of a scientist? Explain why or why not.

   _____

   _____

3. What might a scientist want to know about the stars?

   _____

   _____

4. What might a scientist want to know about the spider?

   _____

   _____

5. Choose one of the poems, and rewrite it from the point of view of a scientist.

   _____

   _____

   _____

   _____

   _____

   _____

   _____

Walt Whitman's Poetry
Selection Test A

Critical Reading *Identify the letter of the choice that best answers the question.*

____ 1. Which element contributes most to Whitman's poetry of free verse?
   A. regular metrical feet
   B. fixed-length stanzas
   C. regular speech patterns
   D. exact rhyme schemes

____ 2. What can you conclude about Whitman's attitude about himself from these lines from "Song of Myself"?

   I celebrate myself, and sing myself, / And what I assume you shall assume, / For every atom belonging to me as good belongs to you.

   A. He believes in talking about himself.
   B. He is content with who he is.
   C. He thinks he is better than others.
   D. He does not understand science.

____ 3. Which elements of free verse are found in this passage from "Song of Myself"?

   I, now thirty-seven years old in perfect health begin, / Hoping to cease not till death.

   I.   irregular meter
   II. exact rhyme
   III. natural speech cadence
   IV. irregular line length
   A. I, II, IV
   B. I, II, III
   C. I, III, IV
   D. II, III, IV

____ 4. What is the poet's attitude toward nature as expressed in this passage from "Song of Myself"?

   The sharp-hoof'd moose of the north, the cat on the house-sill,
      the chickadee, the prairie dog,
   The litter of the grunting sow as they tug at her teats,
   The brood of the turkey hen and she with her half-spread wings,
   I see in them and myself the same old law.

   A. He divides nature between domestic and wild animals.
   B. He sees all creatures, including humans, as part of nature.
   C. He thinks nature must continue to grow, or it will die.
   D. He thinks there is no law to control the natural world.

_____ 5. Why does the poet leave the lecture in "When I Heard the Learn'd Astronomer"?
   A. He wants to check the astronomer's facts for accuracy.
   B. He has fallen ill and must go outside to get some air.
   C. He wants to see the stars instead of hearing about them.
   D. He thinks the speaker does not deserve all the applause.

_____ 6. What two elements are seen in a procession in "By the Bivouac's Fitful Flame"?
   A. soldiers and thoughts
   B. wind and fire
   C. loved ones and trees
   D. ghosts and flames

_____ 7. Based on "I Hear American Singing," how does Whitman seem to feel toward the people in the poem?
   A. unfriendly
   B. annoyed
   C. bored
   D. kindly

_____ 8. What class of workers does Whitman focus on in "I Hear American Singing"?
   A. singers
   B. laborers
   C. housewives
   D. athletes

Vocabulary and Grammar

_____ 9. In which sentence is the meaning of the word *effuse* expressed?
   A. Whitman's poetry symbolizes America for many readers.
   B. His poems pour out feelings for both the human and natural world.
   C. Whitman worked as a nurse in a hospital during the Civil War.
   D. One of his poems expresses grief at the death of Lincoln.

_____ 10. Which of the following sentences would need to be corrected so that the pronoun and antecedent agree?
   A. She wrote a poem about her experiences as an astronomer.
   B. They sang as they worked at their daily labors.
   C. He watched a spider and compared it with their soul.
   D. We made camp and watched shadows in our campfire.

Essay

11. Whitman's Preface to the 1855 Edition of "Leaves of Grass" communicates his belief that America benefits from all the different nationalities that make up its population. America was different from many other countries that had people from similar backgrounds. Write a brief essay that gives examples from your personal experience or reading that support Whitman's beliefs.

12. Readers of Whitman's poetry see him as a poet who celebrated life. Do you think this is true? Write a brief essay stating whether you think Whitman's poetry celebrates life and is positive in its approach. Give at least two examples from his poetry to support your opinion.

Walt Whitman's Poetry
Selection Test B

Critical Reading *Identify the letter of the choice that best completes the statement or answers the question.*

____ 1. When Whitman states, in the preface to the 1855 edition of *Leaves of Grass*, that "The United States themselves are essentially the greatest poem," he supports his opinion by citing
   A. the vitality and diversity of Americans.
   B. the rhythmic speech patterns of Americans.
   C. American respect for literary traditions.
   D. his own popularity as a poet.

____ 2. Based on the following passage from the preface to the 1855 edition of *Leaves of Grass*, what can you infer about Whitman's attitude toward the past?

   America does not repel the past or what it has produced under its forms or amid other politics or the idea of castes or the old religions . . . accepts the lesson with calmness . . . is not so impatient as has been supposed that the slough still sticks to opinions and manners and literature while the life which served its requirements has passed into the new life of the new forms.

   A. Whitman does not think Americans have anything to learn from the past.
   B. Whitman thinks Americans should study the past for its own sake.
   C. Whitman wishes Americans would follow past traditions more carefully.
   D. Whitman is pleased Americans learn from the past while making a new way of life.

____ 3. Structurally speaking, what makes "Song of Myself" a typical Whitman poem?
   A. its complex meter
   B. its use of regular stanzas
   C. its use of lines of fixed lengths
   D. its use of the natural cadences of human speech

____ 4. In "Song of Myself," when the speaker says "I, now thirty-seven years old in perfect health begin, / Hoping to cease not till death," what do you think he is beginning?
   A. communicating with nature
   B. a family
   C. reading poetry
   D. writing poetry

____ 5. What can you infer about the poet's attitude from these lines in "Song of Myself"?

   These are really the thoughts of all men in all ages and lands, they are not original with me, / If they are not yours as much as mine they are nothing, or next to nothing. . . .

   A. Whitman is pleased to acknowledge that he borrowed ideas in "Song of Myself" from another poet.
   B. Whitman believes that his observations are, in some sense, universally shared.
   C. Whitman believes that he can predict what people who read his poetry in the future will think.
   D. Whitman thinks that his poetry is worthless if readers disagree with him.

____ 6. The phrase "barbaric yawp" in "Song of Myself" is an example of Whitman's
   A. pessimism.
   B. love of nature.
   C. informality.
   D. British roots as a poet.

____ 7. Based on the details in "Song of Myself" and "I Hear America Singing," what can you infer about Whitman's attitude toward other people?
   A. He feels affectionate toward other people.
   B. He does not like to be around people.
   C. He is bossy and likes to control the people around him.
   D. He thinks that most people are very foolish.

____ 8. "The singing" the speaker hears in "I Hear America Singing" is
   A. the language of different ethnic groups in the American melting pot.
   B. the songs from foreign lands brought to America by immigrants.
   C. the poetry of Whitman and other American poets.
   D. the individuality of Americans in different walks of life.

____ 9. In "When I Heard the Learn'd Astronomer," the speaker moves from
   A. optimism to pessimism.
   B. the world of intellect to the world of wonder.
   C. Transcendentalism to mysticism.
   D. certitude to doubt.

____ 10. The central comparison in "A Noiseless Patient Spider" is between
   A. the spider and the speaker's soul.
   B. the spider and the filament.
   C. the spider's promontory and the speaker's isolated location.
   D. the spider's filament and the soul's gossamer thread.

____ 11. Free verse is especially suited to "A Noiseless Patient Spider" because it reflects
   A. the spider's noiselessness.
   B. the spider's patience.
   C. the spider's activity of launching forth filament.
   D. the isolation of the spider and the soul.

____ 12. From the details in "A Noiseless Patient Spider," you can infer that Whitman admires the spider for its ability to
   A. use its body to explore its surroundings.
   B. quietly and patiently capture the insects it will eat.
   C. create beautiful silken web patterns.
   D. move from place to place without being noticed.

____ 13. Which of the following was *not* a prime reason why Whitman chose to write in free verse?
   A. to express his individuality
   B. to celebrate democracy
   C. to convey a sense of freedom
   D. to imitate earlier poets he admired

___ 14. Based on his poetry, what can you infer about Whitman's attitude toward nature?
      I. He admires nature.
     II. He learns from nature.
    III. He considers himself to be part of nature.
    IV. He likes to spend time outdoors.
    A. I and II only
    B. II and III only
    C. I, III, and IV only
    D. I, II, III, and IV

Vocabulary and Grammar

___ 15. What does the speaker in "Song of Myself" mean when he says that he holds "creeds and schools in *abeyance*"?
    A. He goes to school regularly.
    B. He has temporarily let go of philosophies he learned in school.
    C. He detests creeds and schools.
    D. He thinks that Americans of all creeds should spend more time in school.

___ 16. Who seems to be stealthily watching the speaker in these lines from "By the Bivouac's Fitful Flame"?

    Like a phantom far or near an occasional figure moving,
    The shrubs and trees, (as I lift my eyes they seem to be stealthily watching me,)
    While wind in procession thoughts, O tender and wondrous thoughts. . . .

    A. the enemy
    B. a phantom or an occasional figure
    C. the shrubs and trees
    D. the speaker's eyes

Essay

17. Suppose Whitman had written "I Hear America Singing" today. How would the poem be different? Write an essay describing the differences.

18. Use the information in "Song of Myself" to infer Whitman's attitude toward death. Then write an essay explaining his attitude. Be sure to cite examples of language and details that point to the general attitude you describe.

19. How does Whitman's poetry reflect his feelings about democracy? Address this question in an essay that cites examples from at least two of Whitman's poems in your texts. Include in your discussion not only the content of the poems but also their structure or form.

Writing About Literature—Unit 3
Compare and Contrast Literary Trends

Prewriting: Analyzing Similarities and Differences

Use the chart below to closely analyze specific features of the selections you have chosen.

Unique to _____	Similarities	Unique to _____

Drafting: Devising an Outline

Use the information from your chart to complete the working outline below.

    I. Similarities between _____ and _____

        A.

        B.

        C.

        D.

    II. Differences between _____ and _____

        A.

        B.

        C.

        D.

Writing About Literature—Unit 3

Compare and Contrast Literary Trends: Integrating Grammar Skills

Review your draft to evaluate sentence structure and variety. If you find too many long sentences in a row, break some of them down into shorter sentences. If you find a string of short, choppy sentences, combine some of them. Use varied sentence beginnings, so that not every sentence begins with the subject, followed by the verb.

Repetitive: American writing flourished during the 1800s. Poe wrote disturbing horror stories. Emerson produced striking essays.

Improved: During the 1800s, American writing flourished. Poe wrote disturbing horror stories, while Emerson produced original and striking essays.

Identifying Repetitive Sentence Patterns

A. DIRECTIONS: *In the blank, write whether each group of sentences is* repetitive *or* varied.

_____ 1. Washington Irving was a Romantic writer. James Fenimore Cooper was also one of the Romantics. William Cullen Bryant was part of Romanticism too.

_____ 2. A character with moral integrity, Cooper's Natty Bumppo loved nature rather than civilization. This preference became a major theme in American literature.

_____ 3. Thoreau went to live by himself at Walden Pond. He described what he saw at Walden Pond. He wrote essays about individuality and simplicity at Walden Pond.

Fixing Repetitive Sentence Patterns

B. DIRECTIONS: *Rewrite each passage to include sentences of varied length and structure.*

1. Nathaniel Hawthorne did not have an optimistic view of life. Herman Melville did not have an optimistic view of life either. They were not like the Transcendentalists.

_____

_____

_____

2. Emily Dickinson was a hermit for much of her life. Emily Dickinson did not publish her poetry. She wrote in order to struggle privately with questions of life and death.

_____

_____

_____

Writing Workshop—Unit 3
Narration: Reflective Essay

Prewriting: Narrowing Your Topic

Use the chart below to focus your writing on a specific event and the insight you gained.

List a moment from your life that you want to explore.	
What is an insight you gained from your experience?	
Did you learn something new about yourself? What?	
Did you see the world in a different light? How?	
Write a sentence that identifies the event and the lesson learned.	

Drafting: Providing Elaboration

Thoughts you had during the event →	
Feelings you experienced during the event →	
Sensory images you remember from the event →	

Use the diagram below to help you add details to your essay to make your essay more substantial.

Writing Workshop—Unit 3
Reflective Essay: Integrating Grammar Skills

Revising Your Sentences

Even though your reflective essay is about an event that happened to you, avoid beginning every sentence with *I*. **Vary sentence beginnings** to make your writing more interesting. You may need to combine some sentences to avoid a string of short, simple sentences that begin the same way.

Boring:	I remember the door. I remember it was locked. I remember being curious.
More interesting:	The door was locked, and I remember being curious.
Boring:	I walked into the room. I looked around. I saw a piano.
More interesting:	When I walked into the room, I looked around and saw a piano.

Fixing Problem Sentences

DIRECTIONS: *Rewrite each passage to create varied sentence beginnings. You may need to combine some sentences.*

1. I heard the wind. I heard it howling. I heard the front door suddenly slam. I heard the windows rattling.

   _____

   _____

   _____

2. Making choices is hard. Making choices is important. Making choices is part of growing up.

   _____

   _____

3. My big sister is my best friend. My big sister really listens to me. My big sister gives me advice when I ask for it. My big sister usually lets me make my own decisions.

   _____

   _____

   _____

   _____

Spelling—Unit 3
Proofreading Practice

DIRECTIONS: *Proofread the following passage, looking for 16 misspelled words. Cross out each misspelled word, and write it correctly in the space above.*

More than 100 feet long, the blue whale is the largest animal in the world. The dimentions of other whales vary. Pilot whales measure about 28 feet, while dolphins, members of the whale family, can be as small as three feet long. Whales are mammals, and imature whales nurse on their mother's milk. Whales are divisable into two main groups: toothed whales and baleen whales, which have no teeth.

Possessers of lungs, not gills, whales must surface in order to breath. When they reach the surface, they expel a visable cloud of moisture, called a spout. Whales are also known for the lithe, graceful motions of their tails, which are controlled by powerful musles. Their body shape gives them great efficiency in moving threw the water.

Some of the most reliable information collected about whales comes from centuries of commershal whale hunters, rather than from sientists. Herman Melville, the author of *Moby Dick*, was himself an ex sailor who served on the crew of a whaling ship.

We know that whales are social animals that are capable of communication, espeshally when they are in trouble. They use barks, whistles, screams, and clicks of different frequencies.

It is a disturbing experience to view a whale that has become stranded on a beach. A whale is dependant on deep water in order to move. Often, it is impossable for people to get a beached whale back into the ocean. Meanwhile, the whale cries out for assistance, and other whales become stranded while trying to help. Probable explanations for beaching include interferance with the whale's echolocation system, which may be caused by disease, underwater explosians, or other disturbances.

Name _____ Date _____

Analyzing Media

For each television show you view, fill out a copy of the following chart to help you analyze the show's purpose, audience, and techniques.

Name of television program: _____

What is the main purpose of the program?
Who is the intended audience for this program?
What language is used that signals the purpose of the program?
What techniques are used?
Are the techniques effective? Why or why not?

Suggestions For Further Reading—Unit 3

DIRECTIONS: *Think about the books suggested for this Unit that you have read. Then, on a separate sheet of paper, answer the discussion questions and take notes for your literature circle.*

The Journals of Lewis and Clark edited by John Bakeless

Discussion Rivers are an important entry in the journals. In a group, discuss the difficulties that rivers posed to the party of Lewis and Clark.

Connections—Literature Circle Form a panel to discuss the significance of the Lewis and Clark expedition. Assign each panel member a different role: Native American leader, American politician, scientist, future settler, conservationist, or historian. After the presentations, other class members can pose questions to the panel.

The Scarlet Letter by Nathaniel Hawthorne

Discussion *The Scarlet Letter* has been called "the last great novel of responsibility." Use specific events and characterizations from the text to defend or refute this statement.

Connections—Literature Circle Discuss the role that shame played in enforcing the prevailing social morals in Hester Prynne's community. Use your reading of the book to consider whether shame is ever an effective and justified method for controlling people's behavior. What are the advantages and disadvantages of this form of social control?

Selected Writings of Ralph Waldo Emerson

Discussion In a small group, discuss whether you agree with Emerson's claim that being self-reliant and living according to your principles the only way to find peace.

Connections—Literature Circle Hold a roundtable discussion about how Emerson might view trends on conformism and materialism in modern American society. For example, would he view modern politics and popular culture as embodying or contradicting the values he espouses in his writing? Use examples from the book to support your opinions.

Walden and Civil Disobedience by Henry David Thoreau

Discussion In a small group, discuss the following question: What specific ideas in *Walden* could inspire modern environmentalists, as well as advocates of spiritual renewal?

Connections—Literature Circle Consider the civil rights leader, Martin Luther King, Jr. and the Indian leader Mahatma Gandhi. How successful was Dr. King or Gandhi in applying Thoreau's ideas? What problems and limitations became apparent when Thoreau's concept of civil disobedience was translated into action?

Leaves of Grass by Walt Whitman

Discussion Discuss your reactions to Whitman's language and imagery and to the structure of the poems. What did you find surprising or unique about Whitman's poetry?

Connections—Literature Circle In a group, discuss the following questions: What do poems such as "I Hear America Singing" tell us about Whitman's America? Do any of these things remain true about modern America?

Unit 3: A Growing Nation
Benchmark Test 4

MULTIPLE CHOICE

Literary Analysis and Reading Skills *Read the selection. Then, answer the questions that follow.*

Guides know about enough English to tangle everything up so that a man can make neither head nor tail of it. They know their story by heart—the history of every statue, painting, cathedral, or other wonder they show you. They know it and tell it as a parrot would—and if you interrupt, and throw them off the track, they have to go back and begin over again. All their lives long, they are employed in showing strange things to foreigners and listening to their bursts of admiration. It is human nature to take delight in exciting admiration. It is what prompts children to say "smart" things, and do absurd ones, and in other ways "show off" when company is present. It is what makes gossips turn out in rain and storm to go and be the first to tell a startling bit of news. Think, then what a passion it becomes with a guide, whose privilege it is, every day, to show to strangers wonders that throw them into perfect ecstasies of admiration! He gets so that he could not by any possibility live in a soberer atmosphere. After we discovered this, we *never* went into ecstasies any more—we never admired anything—we never showed any but impassible faces and stupid indifference in the presence of the sublimest wonders a guide had to display.

from *The Innocents Abroad* by Mark Twain

1. How might a reader challenge the author's text in this selection?
   A. Evaluate Twain's choice of words in the selection.
   B. Compare's Twain's opinion with that of others who have employed guides.
   C. Compare this selection with other works by Twain.
   D. Determine the author's purpose for writing the selection.

2. Which of these is an effective way to challenge the following assertion from the selection?

   "Guides know about enough English to tangle everything up so that a man can make neither head nor tail of it."

   A. Identify and evaluate the theme of the selection.
   B. Analyze other literary works on similar subjects.
   C. Use your own words to paraphrase the statement.
   D. Evaluate Twain's evidence for the assertion.

3. What is one aspect of the author's style in this selection?
   A. He uses a somber tone.
   B. He varies the point of view.
   C. He uses mostly short sentences.
   D. He uses exaggeration to add humor.

4. What detail does the author use to support his philosophy that humans "take delight in exciting admiration"?
   A. Children like to show off.
   B. Guides memorize their stories.
   C. Guides show strange things to others.
   D. People admire what guides show them.

Read the selection. Then, answer the questions that follow.

The morns are meeker than they were,
The nuts are getting brown;
The berry's cheek is plumper,
The rose is out of town.
The maple wears a gayer scarf,
The field a scarlet gown.
Lest I should be old-fashioned,
I'll put a trinket on.

LXXIX by Emily Dickinson

5. What do the nuts, berry, rose, maple, and field symbolize in the poem?
   A. change
   B. youth
   C. nature
   D. autumn

6. Which of these best describes the poet's style in this poem?
   A. formal
   B. concise
   C. wordy
   D. flowery

7. Which of these is an example of slant rhyme from the poem?
   A. meeker, cheek
   B. gown, on
   C. brown, town
   D. were, plumper

8. Which of these best describes the concept conveyed by the images in the poem?
   A. the need to conform
   B. the inevitability of change
   C. the beauty of the natural world
   D. the pleasures of decoration

9. Which of these best describes the poet's attitude toward her subject in the poem?
   A. admiration
   B. sadness
   C. surprise
   D. disappointment

Read the selection. Then, answer the questions that follow.

> Eldorado was an imaginary place abounding in gold, thought
> by sixteenth-century Spaniards to exist in America.
>
> Gaily bedight,
> A gallant knight,
> In sunshine and in shadow,
> Had journey long,
> Singing a song,
> In search of Eldorado.
>
> But he grew old,
> This knight so bold,
> And o'er his heart a shadow
> Fell as he found
> No spot of ground
> That looked like Eldorado.
>
> from "Eldorado" by Edgar Allan Poe

10. What does Eldorado most likely symbolize in the poem?
    A. death
    B. fulfillment
    C. beauty
    D. creation

11. Which of these does *shadow* most likely symbolize in the first stanza of the poem?
    A. adversity
    B. dreams
    C. protection
    D. hope

12. What idea do the images in the poem's second stanza convey?
    A. despair
    B. hopefulness
    C. acceptance
    D. regret

13. The *journey* in this poem is a symbol for life. Which of these best describes this type of symbol in literature?
   A. simile
   B. theme
   C. archetype
   D. diction

14. Which of these is a feature of free verse in poetry?
   A. a lack of sound devices
   B. the use of symbolism
   C. fixed meter and line length
   D. an irregular pattern of rhyme and meter

15. Which line of poetry is characteristic of transcendentalism?
   A. "All great heroes have their fall"
   B. "Let none but intuition be your guide"
   C. "A word is dead, when it is said"
   D. "In my world the dead were out of range"

Vocabulary

16. Based on your knowledge of the prefix *mal-*, what is the meaning of *malfunction*?
   A. unusual appearance
   B. failure to operate normally
   C. limited use
   D. heightened performance

17. Using your knowledge of the root *-fus-*, what is the meaning of *suffused*?
   A. filled
   B. heated
   C. cheerful
   D. lively

18. Which of these best defines *infinite* in the following sentence, based on your knowledge of the meaning of the root *-finis-*?

   To his first-period teacher, Kevis seemed to have an infinite supply of tardiness excuses.

   A. endless
   B. creative
   C. dwindling
   D. available

19. Based on your knowledge of the root *-flu-*, what is the meaning of *fluidity*?
    A. in a hurried manner
    B. free of self-consciousness
    C. showing great strength
    D. characterized by a flowing style

20. What is the likely meaning of *radiance* in the following sentence, based on your knowledge of the root *-radi-*?

    Carlos was distracted by the radiance of Lina's smile.

    A. beauty
    B. friendliness
    C. brightness
    D. power

Grammar

21. Which sentence shows correct agreement of a collective noun and its verb?
    A. The orchestra is taking their places on the stage.
    B. The class is presently holding elections.
    C. The committee is arguing about goals for the coming year.
    D. The jury expect its verdict to be controversial.

22. In which sentence does the verb agree with its subject?
    A. The team are winning by two points.
    B. Martha's family is traveling to Ohio.
    C. The faculty meet once each month.
    D. Another flock were seen flying north.

23. What is the infinitive phrase in the following sentence?

    Ms. Bell went to the mayor's office to complain about his treatment of the protestors.

    A. to the mayor's office
    B. to complain
    C. about his treatment
    D. of the protestors

24. What is the function of the gerund in the following sentence?

    In order to be skilled at debating, one has to practice often.

    A. direct object
    B. predicate nominative
    C. subject
    D. object of a preposition

25. Which sentence shows correct pronoun and antecedent agreement?

    A. Bo looked at CD players but decided that he couldn't afford it.

    B. Either Kim or Rachel will have the party at their house.

    C. Members of the club must pay her dues to the treasurer.

    D. Mom and Dad spend their free time cycling and swimming.

26. What is the antecedent of the pronoun *his* in the following sentence?

Neither Alex nor John has completed his application for the summer job.

    A. Alex, John

    B. Alex

    C. John

    D. neither

ESSAY

27. Choose one of these characters from real life, a book, or a movie: an interesting family member, a heroic person, an admirable person, an athlete, a celebrity. Make a list of what makes that person interesting.

28. On a separate sheet of paper, write a draft of a letter to an author whose work you admire. You may want to write about a specific literary work. In your letter, explain what you admire about the work and ask any questions you may have.

29. How would you complete the following statement? *I think that there should be a law against* _____. Imagine that you will use this statement as the basis for an editorial for a major newsmagazine. On a separate sheet of paper, write your completed statement. Then, list at least three distinct examples that support your point of view.

ANSWERS

Diagnostic Test 3, p. 2

MULTIPLE CHOICE

1. ANS: B
2. ANS: D
3. ANS: B
4. ANS: D
5. ANS: B
6. ANS: C
7. ANS: A
8. ANS: C
9. ANS: A
10. ANS: B
11. ANS: D
12. ANS: B
13. ANS: B
14. ANS: C
15. ANS: D

Unit 3 Introduction

Names and Terms to Know, p. 5

A. 1. F; 2. A; 3. E; 4. G; 5. B; 6. C; 7. D; 8. H

B. Sample Answers

1. Alexis de Tocqueville was originally sent to America to report on its prisons. Instead, he was struck by the energy of the new nation and its faith in a hopeful future, so he wrote about that.

2. Sacajawea, a Shoshone Indian, was a key factor in the success of the exploration of Lewis and Clark. In addition to acting as a guide, she could translate for them and knew how to gather wild food and herbs to sustain them.

3. The Seneca Falls Convention was held in 1848, in part as a reaction to the laws forbidding women to vote or file a lawsuit.

4. The best-known Transcendentalists were Emerson and Thoreau, New England writers. Emerson focused on the Over-Soul, and Thoreau, who lived alone at Walden Pond, focused on writing about simplicity.

Focus Questions, p. 6

Sample Answers

1. As the nation grew from its origins on the East coast, it began to think of itself as a grand place filled with great responsibilities—both nationally and internationally. At home, the emphasis was on expansion and individual freedom (limited to white males). In the world, America fought against Great Britain and Mexico as it struggled to establish strength and power.

2. The physical growth of the new nation meant that people had to travel farther and communicate across longer distances. These challenges were addressed by the cre-ation of canals, turnpikes, railroads, and the telegraph system. In addition, as factories developed, the challenge of finding inexpensive labor was answered by the practice of putting children to work and creating unsafe working conditions.

3. The literature of the period reflected both support for, and reaction against, the nation's expansion. Support and hopefulness were expressed in the work of Walt Whitman, who celebrated the optimism and growth of America. Other writers, such as the Romanticists and the Transcendentalists, focused on subjects such as nature that suggested a simpler approach to life. In addition, some writers—Emerson, Whittier, Melville, and Lowell—wrote against slavery, which was an issue that grew in importance as the nation grew.

"The Devil and Tom Walker"
by Washington Irving

Vocabulary Warm-up Exercises, p. 8

A.
1. indifference
2. zeal
3. meager
4. notorious
5. prone
6. prior
7. consequence
8. elapsed

B. Sample Answers

1. F; A statement is a <u>contradiction</u> if it opposes, not agrees, with another.

2. T; For a fierce competitor, winning is <u>uppermost</u>, or primary.

3. T; A nurse performs <u>steadfastly</u>, without change, by remaining with a patient all night.

4. T; Someone who is <u>squeamish</u> would be unable to eat slimy things.

5. T; A seatbelt is a <u>precaution</u>, or care taken in advance.

6. F; If a sport is too <u>strenuous</u>, it takes too much energy.

7. F; A letter that <u>disclosed</u> the truth revealed it.

8. F; A disease that is <u>prevalent</u> is common among people.

Reading Warm-up A, p. 9

Sample Answers

1. (enthusiasm); Students may say that they play sports, dance, or read with *zeal*.

2. <u>celebrate</u>, [not] <u>harmless and obscure</u>; Students may say that someone may be *notorious* for crime, ignorance, or bad fashion.

3. (tending to); I am *prone* to believe anyone who is a good storyteller.

4. scarce; Students may say that there may be a *meager* supply of food, clothes, or ideas.

5. (the overall effect of the satires was very scattered and random); Students may say that one possible *consequence* of winning the lottery is quitting one's job or buying a new house.

6. such a short time; Students may say that twenty-four hours have *elapsed* since their last English class.

7. (not caring at all); Students may say that they feel only *indifference* toward a certain sport, award show, or art form.

8. before; *Prior* to lunch, students may wash their hands or have gym.

Reading Warm-up B, p. 10

Sample Answers

1. reveal; Students may note that the identity of a spy or the cause of an accident was recently *disclosed*.

2. (opposing, opposing, opposing); "Contra" in *contradiction* indicates being against.

3. existed widely; Students may say that one *prevalent* attitude in school is that the cafeteria food needs improving.

4. An antonym for *uppermost* is *lowermost*.

5. Efforts had to be *strenuous*, requiring great effort, just to survive starvation, harsh winters, disease, and conflict with Native Americans; *vigorous, energetic.*

6. (care); One common *precaution* is to look both ways before crossing the street.

7. (too sensitive); Students may say that many people are *squeamish* about watching a gory movie or about cleaning up after pets.

8. with firm resolve; Despite a series of failures, the director of the project continued *steadfastly* to encourage the team.

Literary Analysis: Omniscient Point of View, p. 11

Sample Responses

1. Tom was so greedy that he usually never worried about the consequences. This time, however, he was more cautious.

2. He usually didn't share experiences with his wife, but because this secret made him uneasy, he willingly shared it.

3. Tom's wife was so greedy that she wanted Tom to make a deal with the Devil so they could have money.

4. Tom decided not to make the deal strictly to be contrary and go against his wife's wishes.

5. Tom's wife was headstrong as well as greedy. She decided to take the offer that the Devil made and keep all the money for herself.

6. The Devil was clever. He made Tom wait a long time so that Tom would be desperate and agree to anything.

Reading Strategy: Infer Cultural Attitudes, p. 12

Suggested Responses

1. In the early 1700s apparently husbands and wives shared the household as common property.

2. Intolerance of religious attitudes was prevalent during this era, an era that also saw many Americans engaged in the slave trade and some involved in witch hunts—all behavior that Irving considers "of the devil."

3. People believed that God used nature to punish them, as in earthquakes.

4. Greed was very much a part of life in New England, at least in Irving's eyes. Irving is warning them in this story about Tom Walker.

Vocabulary Builder, p. 13

A. 1. export; 2. extrovert; 3. exhale; 4. exoskeleton; 5. extract; 6. extricate

B. 1. A; 2. C; 3. D; 4. C; 5. D

Grammar and Style: Adjective Clauses, p. 14

A. 1. that took place

2. which made it dark at noonday

3. which afforded precarious footholds among deep sloughs

4. which they had looked upon as almost impregnable

5. who had waxed wealthy by driving shrewd bargains with the Indians

B. Sample Responses

1. She greatly admired her teacher, who could answer all the questions students asked.

2. The man felt compassion for the stranger, whose eyes showed great sorrow.

3. They were astounded by the action, which was totally unexpected.

4. He was captivated by the child, whose eyes were clear and calm.

5. She pointed at the statue that rose majestically over the harbor.

Enrichment: Narrative Point of View, p. 17

Students should indicate three scenes from "The Devil and Tom Walker." For each scene, students should describe a technique or techniques they would use to film it, keeping the viewpoint of the omniscient narrator in mind. For example, if students choose the scene where the Devil first confronts Tom, they might decide to open the scene with close-up views of thick, foreboding foliage, from Tom's point of view. Blinks could be represented by quick, black frames. They could look down on the stick, and the skull that is uncovered. Until this point, only "nature" sounds would be heard and a soft "Humph" from Tom. All of a sudden a loud, booming voice says, "Let that skull alone!"

Selection Test A, p. 18

Critical Reading

1. ANS: D	DIF: Easy	OBJ: Literary Analysis
2. ANS: B	DIF: Easy	OBJ: Reading Strategy
3. ANS: A	DIF: Easy	OBJ: Interpretation
4. ANS: C	DIF: Easy	OBJ: Comprehension
5. ANS: B	DIF: Easy	OBJ: Reading Strategy
6. ANS: C	DIF: Easy	OBJ: Reading Strategy
7. ANS: C	DIF: Easy	OBJ: Interpretation
8. ANS: B	DIF: Easy	OBJ: Literary Analysis

Vocabulary and Grammar

9. ANS: B	DIF: Easy	OBJ: Vocabulary
10. ANS: D	DIF: Easy	OBJ: Grammar

Essay

11. Students' essays should reflect that Tom and his wife are one-dimensional characters. Their chief motivation at the beginning of the story is greed and they continue to be greedy until their respective deaths. They change only in the way that they seek to be rich. Tom's wife originally hopes that Tom will make a pact with the Devil and make them both rich. When he does not, she goes off to try to make a deal for herself. Tom makes different decisions about how he will become rich, but his greed remains constant.

    Difficulty: *Easy*

    Objective: *Essay*

12. Students who believe Tom deserved his fate may say that he was greedy, unpleasant, and made money as a moneylender. Also, he made a pact with the Devil, so he knew what he was doing. Students who don't believe Tom deserved his fate may say that no one deserves to be taken to Hell, and that Tom was only trying to get rich like everyone else. Moneylending may have been unpopular in the days when this story was written, but today people lend money, and it is not considered evil.

    Difficulty: *Easy*

    Objective: *Essay*

Selection Test B, p. 21

Critical Reading

1. ANS: A	DIF: Challenging	OBJ: Interpretation
2. ANS: B	DIF: Average	OBJ: Comprehension
3. ANS: D	DIF: Average	OBJ: Interpretation
4. ANS: D	DIF: Average	OBJ: Comprehension
5. ANS: A	DIF: Average	OBJ: Interpretation
6. ANS: C	DIF: Challenging	OBJ: Interpretation
7. ANS: D	DIF: Average	OBJ: Interpretation
8. ANS: B	DIF: Average	OBJ: Reading Strategy
9. ANS: B	DIF: Challenging	OBJ: Reading Strategy

10. ANS: D	DIF: Challenging	OBJ: Literary Analysis
11. ANS: C	DIF: Average	OBJ: Literary Analysis
12. ANS: A	DIF: Challenging	OBJ: Reading Strategy
13. ANS: C	DIF: Challenging	OBJ: Literary Analysis

Vocabulary and Grammar

14. ANS: D	DIF: Easy	OBJ: Vocabulary
15. ANS: C	DIF: Easy	OBJ: Grammar
16. ANS: C	DIF: Average	OBJ: Vocabulary
17. ANS: A	DIF: Easy	OBJ: Vocabulary

Essay

18. Students should realize that the tree was the one with Tom Walker's name carved on it. They should cite details that suggest that the Devil carves on the trees the names of the souls he owns and, upon death, destroys the tree by burning.

    Difficulty: *Easy*

    Objective: *Essay*

19. Students may point out that the use of an omniscient narrator allows Irving to make clear the motives and desires of the different characters and also to make general comments on the morals of the characters and the times. Students should give examples that illustrate different characters' thoughts and perceptions and the narrator's general comments. Students should make clear that without an omniscient narrator, some of these important story elements would be absent; others would have to be revealed indirectly, through dialogue and action.

    Difficulty: *Average*

    Objective: *Essay*

20. Students will probably hypothesize that the possessions disappeared or were destroyed because the Devil took back his wealth, perhaps out of spite or to use again on another victim. Information about the Devil's craftiness should be used in the explanation.

    Difficulty: *Challenging*

    Objective: *Essay*

"The Tide Rises, The Tide Falls"
by Henry Wadsworth Longfellow
"Thanatopsis" by William Cullen Bryant
"Old Ironsides" by Oliver Wendell Holmes
from *Snowbound* by John Greenleaf Whittier

Vocabulary Warm-up Exercises, p. 25

A. 1. din
2. earnest
3. strife
4. transfigured
5. mournful
6. splendor

Unit 3 Resources: A Growing Nation

7. sublime
8. waning

B. Sample Answers

1. If you <u>efface</u> a name from a monument, you completely remove it, so it would not be readable.
2. Because someone who is <u>pensive</u> is thinking seriously about something, he definitely has something on his mind.
3. Scientists would consider rumbling a <u>portent</u>, or sign, that a volcano was about to erupt.
4. Yes, a look of <u>reproach</u> is a look of blame or accusation.
5. No, a new coat would not be <u>threadbare</u>, or worn and shabby.
6. No, if you <u>vanquished</u> your fear, you conquered it and would not be terrified.
7. No, if a dog's obedience is <u>unfaltering</u>, it never wavers or fails.
8. If a snack <u>sustained</u> you, it supported and strengthened you enough to last till dinnertime.

Reading Warm-up A, p. 26

Sample Answers

1. (grief overwhelmed); Antonyms for *mournful* include *joyful* and *happy*.
2. <u>lessening</u>; Enthusiasm may be *waning* for a popular band, movie star, vacation spot, or fashion trend.
3. (struggle); I have been fortunate that there has been so little conflict and *strife* in my life.
4. <u>noise</u>; The restaurant we went to last night was extremely noisy, and the *din* ruined our meal.
5. (awe-inspiring); *Sublime* may be defined as extraordinarily beautiful or even perfect, with a quality that seems unearthly or divine.
6. <u>changed</u>; The root *figure* indicates form or shape.
7. (glory); Students may suggest that a certain building, landscape, spectacle, or performance possesses *splendor*.
8. <u>passion, sincere</u>; Students may describe a situation in which someone claims to be a friend but is not *earnest*.

Reading Warm-up B, p. 27

Sample Answers

1. <u>wipe away</u>; Students may note that time cannot *efface* a great historical accomplishment, an artistic masterpiece, or true love.
2. (triumph); Synonyms for *vanquished* include *conquered* and *defeated*.
3. <u>ragged, full of holes</u>; When his Mom saw that his pants were *threadbare*, she knew he needed new clothes.
4. (blame); "Mark, you were the only reason we came here, and your backing out now ruins the trip for all of us."
5. <u>thought</u>; Someone who is *pensive* may be quiet, even silent, have a furrowed brow, and stare into space.

6. (omen); A bank of dark clouds could be considered a *portent* of a storm, or failing an exam could be a *portent* of failing a course.
7. (unwavering); Students may describe a teacher who inspires students and displays *unfaltering* devotion to ensuring their success.
8. <u>supporting</u>; Students may describe a parent or relative who *sustained* them to realize a dream when everyone else had doubts.

Literary Analysis: Meter, p. 28

The metrical pattern has lines of iambic tetrameter alternating with lines of iambic trimeter.

Oh, bet|ter that| her shat|tered hulk
    Should sink| beneath| the wave;
Her thun|ders shook| the might|y deep,
    And there| should be| her grave;
Nail to| the mast| her hol|y flag.
    Set eve|ry thread| bare sail,
And give| her to| the god| of storms
    The light|ning and| the gale!

Reading Strategy: Summarize, p. 29

Possible Responses

1. Death unites all people no matter their status in life.
2. It would be better if she (the ship Old Ironsides) were sunk at sea with dignity by a storm.

Vocabulary Builder, p. 30

A. 1. A; 2. D

B. replacement words are underlined

1. The darkness that morning was a very <u>ominous</u> prophecy of the snow to come.
2. The valleys were blanketed in a <u>pensive</u> quietness.
3. The rooster looked indignant, and his call seemed almost <u>querulous</u>.
4. The wise, the good, and everyone else are buried now in one mighty <u>sepulcher</u>.
5. The ram ruled the flock of sheep like a biblical <u>patriarch</u>.
6. The letters on the monument were <u>effaced</u> by time.
7. The woods are old and <u>venerable</u>.

Grammar and Style: Participles as Adjectives, p. 31

A. Participles should be underlined and the words they modify should be circled.

1. present, leaning, word modified: miracle
2. past, speckled, word modified: harem
3. past, buried, word modified: brooklet
4. present, blazing, word modified: hearth

B. Sample Responses

1. fascinating book
2. driving rain
3. darkened sky
4. frightened child
5. soothing breeze
6. conquered enemy
7. burning rage
8. draped sleeves

Enrichment: Science p. 34

Suggested Responses

Students should complete the chart with information about curlews and four other birds of the Northeast. Examples of birds that live in the Northeast: American black duck, black-capped chickadee, mallard, northern goshawk, purple finch, ruffed grouse, and saw-whet owl. For each fact, students should say how the fact could be used to help establish a mood.

Selection Test A, p. 35

Critical Reading

1. ANS: A	DIF: Easy	OBJ: Comprehension
2. ANS: B	DIF: Easy	OBJ: Reading Strategy
3. ANS: D	DIF: Easy	OBJ: Literary Analysis
4. ANS: D	DIF: Easy	OBJ: Comprehension
5. ANS: B	DIF: Easy	OBJ: Literary Analysis
6. ANS: C	DIF: Easy	OBJ: Interpretation
7. ANS: B	DIF: Easy	OBJ: Reading Strategy
8. ANS: C	DIF: Easy	OBJ: Literary Analysis
9. ANS: C	DIF: Easy	OBJ: Reading Strategy

Vocabulary and Grammar

10. ANS: C	DIF: Easy	OBJ: Vocabulary
11. ANS: A	DIF: Easy	OBJ: Grammar

Essay

12. Students' essays should reflect the view that Bryant believes that people are buried without respect to their class or importance in human society. Poor people will be buried in the same places as kings, with people of all kinds from different times. Bryant may be suggesting by this that the ways in which people are classified during life make no difference after death. We all end up together, in the same earth.
Difficulty: *Easy*
Objective: *Essay*

13. Students' essays should reflect that Bryant's attitude toward death is not fearful, but accepting. He advises people facing death to take comfort from nature, and to realize that all creatures who have lived, or who will live,

will die and be buried in the same earth. He says that when death comes, people should trust the experience in the same way they trust that they will have pleasant dreams when they go to sleep at night.
Difficulty: *Easy*
Objective: *Essay*

Selection Test B, p. 38

Critical Reading

1. ANS: C	DIF: Easy	OBJ: Comprehension
2. ANS: B	DIF: Challenging	OBJ: Interpretation
3. ANS: A	DIF: Easy	OBJ: Comprehension
4. ANS: D	DIF: Challenging	OBJ: Comprehension
5. ANS: C	DIF: Easy	OBJ: Literary Analysis
6. ANS: A	DIF: Easy	OBJ: Comprehension
7. ANS: B	DIF: Average	OBJ: Interpretation
8. ANS: A	DIF: Average	OBJ: Interpretation
9. ANS: D	DIF: Average	OBJ: Interpretation
10. ANS: D	DIF: Average	OBJ: Reading Strategy
11. ANS: A	DIF: Average	OBJ: Literary Analysis
12. ANS: C	DIF: Challenging	OBJ: Literary Analysis

Vocabulary and Grammar

13. ANS: A	DIF: Average	OBJ: Vocabulary
14. ANS: C	DIF: Challenging	OBJ: Vocabulary
15. ANS: B	DIF: Average	OBJ: Grammar

Essay

16. Most students will probably feel that the poem would be more influential than an editorial. Students may cite examples of Holmes's use of rhythm, rhyme, vivid descriptions, and emotional exclamations—none of which would ordinarily appear in an editorial.
Difficulty: *Easy*
Objective: *Essay*

17. Student responses may discuss how "Thanatopsis" uses nature to build a sense of something larger than the individual and to give a sense of comfort and belonging; how "Old Ironsides" uses images of stormy seas to describe the trials that the ship has undergone and stress its value to the American nation; or how *Snowbound* uses images of a snowstorm to convey a sense of beauty, stresses the storm as a source of privacy and isolation, and contrasts images of the storm and cold with the warmth and security of the speaker's family.
Difficulty: *Challenging*
Objective: *Essay*

"Crossing the Great Divide" by Meriwether Lewis
"The Most Sublime Spectacle on Earth"
by John Wesley Powell

Vocabulary Warm-up Exercises, p. 42

A. 1. duplicated
2. assemblage
3. conspicuous
4. innumerable
5. merchandise
6. afforded
7. portray
8. adequately

B. Sample Answers
1. Because she <u>deemed</u> that book a classic, the critic mentioned it prominently.
2. We lingered at the front in order to photograph the building's impressive <u>façade</u>.
3. We had a warm, almost <u>fraternal</u> relationship with our neighbors.
4. A man of <u>infinite</u> patience, Sal always remained calm, despite provocation.
5. It was a great challenge to make our way through the twists and turns of the <u>labyrinth</u>.
6. The contract was <u>mutually</u> beneficial, with advantages going to both management and labor.
7. To <u>prosecute</u> a project to completion, it is necessary to have a step-by-step plan.
8. Because of its many <u>resources</u>, the foundation had no trouble financing our study trip.

Reading Warm-up A, p. 43

Sample Answers
1. <u>it is nearly impossible . . . or describe this "sublime spectacle"</u>; That novelist used vivid imagery to *portray* memorable characters in her works.
2. (. . . found it difficult to capture the immense vista of the Grand Canyon . . .); *sufficiently*
3. <u>an opportunity to buy it</u>; *offered*
4. <u>the price of . . . once purchased</u>
5. (a collection of the likenesses of flesh-and-blood heroes); *cluster, group*
6. <u>seemingly inexhaustible</u>; *countless*
7. (played a . . . role . . . offered a thrilling view of one of nature's greatest spectacles); The opposite of *conspicuous* is *inconspicuous*.
8. <u>could not have believed that he had . . . the real thing . . . there is no scale that allows the viewer to appreciate the sight</u>; The forger *duplicated* the original painting so skillfully that even some experts believed the fake to be authentic.

Reading Warm-up B, p. 44

Sample Answers
1. <u>in the judgment of historians . . . has been . . . one of the most important contributors</u>; *considered*
2. (departed from St. Louis to . . . their historic exploration of the West); Last summer, Dean decided to <u>prosecute</u> a plan to improve his tennis game.
3. <u>. . . who had been living among the Mandan Indians and enjoyed . . . relations with them</u>; The opposite of *fraternal* is *unfriendly* or *hostile*.
4. <u>plants, fruits, vegetables, and other food . . . for the explorers</u>; *supplies, provisions, means*
5. (amounts of courage, and her patience . . . was said to have no limits); *finite, limited*
6. (or meaningless front); When questioned, the guilty criminal maintained a *façade* of innocence for a while.
7. <u>might otherwise have been a confusing . . . of languages, customs, and cultures</u>; *maze*
8. <u>in which each party maintained a . . . respectful relationship</u>; *jointly*

Literary Analysis: Description, p. 45

1. sight; 2. sight and touch; 3. sight; 4. sound and sight; 5. sound, touch, and sight

Reading Strategy: Note Spatial Relationships, p. 46

Answers to the questions may vary slightly, but students should recognize the basic spatial relationships and underline the terms indicating those relationships.
1. spatial terms: some little distance, down (the river), just below.
   The Indian was some little distance down the river.
   The white men were just below the Indian.
2. spatial terms: between (the cliffs), away
   The blocks were originally between the cliffs.
   Now they have been carried away from the area.
3. spatial terms: below, foundation, crowned
   The black gneiss is below the other layers of rock.
   The limestone is above the other layers of rock.

Vocabulary Builder, p. 47

A. 1. multilingual; 2. Multicolored; 3. multidimensional; 4. multicellular; 5. multinational

B. Sample responses with sample word changes underlined:
1. We took care to make them an <u>obvious</u> object of our own good wishes and the care of our government.
2. Yet all these canyons unite to form one grand canyon, the most <u>inspiring</u> spectacle on the earth.

3. The vast <u>maze</u> of canyon by which the plateau region drained by the Colorado is dissected is also the work of waters.

4. Every river has <u>dug</u> its own gorge.

5. No plane of <u>separation</u> between wall and blue firmament can be seen.

6. The elements that unite to make the Grand Canyon the most sublime spectacle in nature are <u>diverse</u>.

7. The forms are wrought into endless details, to describe which would be a task equal in magnitude to that of describing the stars of the heavens or the <u>numerous</u> beauties of the forest.

Grammar and Style: Participial Phrases, p. 48

A. Students should underline the participial phrases and circle the nouns or pronouns that they modify.

1. participial phrase: composed of many walls; modifies: wall

2. participial phrase: represented in the canyons; modifies: erosion

3. participial phrase: spanning the Grand Canyon with empyrean blue; modifies: dome

B. Sample responses with participial phrases italicized:

1. *Winding through the canyon*, the river made its way to the sea.

2. We raced in canoes *carved from birch bark*.

3. The canyon, *consisting of many smaller canyons*, is a monument to the power of nature.

4. We traveled into a gorge *carved by rushing water*.

Enrichment: Social Studies, p. 51

Sample Responses

1. The Indiana Territory was on the northeastern border of territory gained in the Louisiana Purchase.

2. With the Louisiana Purchase, the border of the western United States changed from the Mississippi River to a line much farther west, formed by the Rocky Mountains.

3. The United States gained direct passage to the Gulf of Mexico with the Louisiana Purchase.

4. Lewis and Clark traveled about 4,400 miles more than they would have if they had traveled in a straight path from St. Louis to the Pacific coast and back. Their trip was about 8,000 miles; a straight-line round trip is about 3,600 miles.

5. The United States had eighteen states at the time of the Louisiana Purchase: Connecticut, Delaware, Georgia, Kentucky, Maine, Maryland, Massachusetts, New Hampshire, New Jersey, New York, North Carolina, Ohio, Pennsylvania, Rhode Island, South Carolina, Tennessee, Vermont, and Virginia.

6. With the addition of the Louisiana Purchase, and then, as a result of its exploration, the acquisition of Oregon Country, the United States gained much territory for westward expansion.

Selection Test A, p. 52

Critical Reading

1. ANS: A	DIF: Easy	OBJ: Comprehension
2. ANS: B	DIF: Easy	OBJ: Literary Analysis
3. ANS: B	DIF: Easy	OBJ: Interpretation
4. ANS: D	DIF: Easy	OBJ: Reading Strategy
5. ANS: A	DIF: Easy	OBJ: Reading Strategy
6. ANS: B	DIF: Easy	OBJ: Literary Analysis
7. ANS: D	DIF: Easy	OBJ: Reading Strategy
8. ANS: C	DIF: Easy	OBJ: Literary Analysis

Vocabulary and Grammar

9. ANS: C	DIF: Easy	OBJ: Vocabulary
10. ANS: C	DIF: Easy	OBJ: Grammar

Essay

11. Students' essays should reflect the historical fact that the U.S. government made many promises to the Native American people, which they did not keep. Lewis says that the Indians are the objects of the good wishes and the care of the government, yet the U.S. military made constant war on Native American nations and wiped most of them out. Lewis says that Native Americans can count on the government for their defense and comfort, yet the U.S. broke every treaty ever made with Indian peoples. Students may suggest that Lewis said the things he did either because he did not know the government would behave as it did, or because he knew it was necessary to win the support of the Native American people in order to complete his exploration.

Difficulty: *Easy*
Objective: *Essay*

12. Students' essays should reflect Powell's intense response to the canyon and also his wish to help others understand what it was like. In using the sense of sound to describe the Grand Canyon as a "land of song," he writes of the movement of water through the canyon, from small musical waterfalls to giant thundering rapids and the continual movement of the river itself.

Difficulty: *Easy*
Objective: *Essay*

Selection Test B, p. 55

Critical Reading

1. ANS: D	DIF: Easy	OBJ: Comprehension
2. ANS: A	DIF: Average	OBJ: Interpretation
3. ANS: D	DIF: Average	OBJ: Interpretation
4. ANS: C	DIF: Easy	OBJ: Literary Analysis
5. ANS: B	DIF: Average	OBJ: Reading Strategy
6. ANS: A	DIF: Easy	OBJ: Comprehension
7. ANS: B	DIF: Challenging	OBJ: Interpretation

8. ANS: D	DIF: Average	OBJ: Comprehension
9. ANS: A	DIF: Challenging	OBJ: Interpretation
10. ANS: B	DIF: Average	OBJ: Literary Analysis
11. ANS: C	DIF: Average	OBJ: Reading Strategy
12. ANS: D	DIF: Challenging	OBJ: Reading Strategy
13. ANS: C	DIF: Average	OBJ: Literary Analysis
14. ANS: B	DIF: Easy	OBJ: Literary Analysis

Vocabulary and Grammar

| 15. ANS: C | DIF: Challenging | OBJ: Vocabulary |
| 16. ANS: C | DIF: Average | OBJ: Grammar |

Essay

17. Students will probably give reasons such as providing the explorers with horses; allowing the explorers to pass peacefully; establishing relations for future trade; and providing the explorers with food, water, directions, and other aid.

Difficulty: *Easy*

Objective: *Essay*

18. Negative experiences might include physical challenges. For example, Powell writes that the Grand Canyon is more difficult to explore than the Himalayas or the Alps. Lewis describes looking for horses in case they could not continue their journey on water. Lewis speaks of having a slight breakfast and sending Shields off to hunt, reminding us that the explorers had to find fresh food along the way. Opinions on explorers' future plans may vary. Students are likely to predict that Powell would be anxious to return to the wilderness and to support their evaluation with his many expressions of wonder and his remark at the end of the selection: "If strength and courage are sufficient for the task, by a year's toil a concept of sublimity can be obtained never again to be equaled on the hither side of Paradise." Students may also feel that Lewis would be interested in returning but should recognize that he is much more businesslike in tone and does not reveal his feelings very much in this selection.

Difficulty: *Average*

Objective: *Essay*

19. Being a geologist, Powell knew how to recognize rocks and rock formations, which probably influenced his report of the layers of rock in the Grand Canyon and how those rocks were formed. The geologist's perspective also contributed to his understanding of the erosion and other factors that created the canyon and may also have added to his sense of time, of the canyon being built over ages. Students may feel that Powell's interest in geology could have prompted him to feel more fascination with the Grand Canyon than an average viewer. They should also recognize that his writings demonstrate a gift for description as well as knowledge about the earth.

Difficulty: *Challenging*

Objective: *Essay*

"The Fall of the House of Usher" and "The Raven" by Edgar Allan Poe

Vocabulary Warm-up Exercises, p. 59

A. 1. maturity
2. alternately
3. similarly
4. enchantment
5. somber
6. sinister
7. boon
8. ghastly

B. Sample Answers
1. T; *Acuteness* connotes keenness, accuracy, and reliability.
2. F; A person exhibiting *apathy* would typically be indifferent.
3. F; *Demeanor* relates to outer appearance and behavior.
4. T; A *gradual* scenario would unfold over time.
5. F; An *inaccessible* office would not be easy to locate and would probably be closed.
6. F; *Sensibility* implies an awareness of the feelings of others.
7. F; *Solace* connotes comfort and a decrease in sorrow or suffering.
8. F; *Succumbed* means "yielded" or "surrendered."

Reading Warm-up A, p. 60

Sample Answers
1. the raven is a gloomy . . . bird; Lane's *somber* expression indicated that he was feeling sad and depressed.
2. (a special sign of favor); an advantage
3. loses all sense of fascination or; positive connotations
4. (terrifying reminder of personal tragedy); *horrible, frightful, grim*
5. (adult birds); *childhood, infancy*
6. the two species are . . . sooty-colored; *comparably, likewise*
7. *by turns;* At summer camp, Stan was *alternately* upbeat and homesick.
8. grim and . . . spreading confusion; *ominous, threatening*

Reading Warm-up B, p. 61

Sample Answers
1. with which a reader keenly experiences this effect; Tom had studied hard, and he answered the exam questions with unusual *acuteness* and accuracy.

2. (with many interruptions from start to finish); The opposite of *gradual* is *rapid* or *sudden*.

3. <u>for the characters and situation</u>

4. <u>or actual indifference;</u> *concern, caring*

5. (ruled out the impact of a single effect); The opposite of *inaccessible* is *accessible.*

6. <u>yielding all his or her attention;</u> *conquered, vanquished*

7. <u>outward</u>

8. (no comfort or); *consolation*

Literary Analysis: Single Effect, p. 62

Sample Responses

1. A. high, narrow, pointed windows
   B. feeble light
   C. "an atmosphere of sorrow"
2. A. the oppressive air
   B. its darkness, dampness, and depth
   C. the grating door
3. A. the light of the storm and of the moon
   B. the widening fissure
   C. the sound of its cracking
4. A. his unusual appearance
   B. his feverish conversation
   C. his odd books
5. A. her pathetic illness
   B. her ghastly passage through Usher's room
   C. her bloodied appearance

Reading Strategy: Break Down Long Sentences, p. 63

1. Suggested core sentence: I had been passing alone through a singularly dreary tract of country and found myself within view of the melancholy House of Usher.

   Sample clarification: Traveling alone through a dreary area, I came within view of the melancholy House of Usher.

2. Suggested core sentence: I reined my horse and gazed down upon the inverted images of the gray sedge, and the ghastly tree stems, and the vacant and eyelike windows.

   Sample clarification: I reined my horse and looked at the gloomy reflection [in the tarn] of the house and landscape.

3. Suggested core sentence: He admitted that much of the peculiar gloom which thus afflicted him could be traced to the severe and long-continued illness—indeed to the evidently approaching dissolution—of a tenderly beloved sister.

   Sample clarification: He admitted that a lot of his gloom was caused by the fatal illness of his beloved sister.

4. Suggested core sentence: Our books were in strict keeping with this character of phantasm.

   Sample clarification: Our books were consistent with our eerie state.

Vocabulary Builder, p. 64

A. Sample Responses

1. When you *advocate* something, you use your voice in support of it.
2. *Vocabulary* refers to the words we know and speak.
3. Something *evocative* calls forth memories or images in our minds.

B. 1. B; 2. C; 3. A; 4. C; 5. C; 6. C; 7. B; 8. C; 9. B

Grammar and Style: Coordinate Adjectives, p. 65

A. 1. C; 2. NC; 3. C; large, liquid, and luminous; 4. NC; 5. C; stern, deep, and irredeemable

B. Sample Responses

1. coordinate: evil, grim, ghastly raven; not coordinate: sleek young raven
2. coordinate: mysterious, ghostly tarn; not coordinate: deep green tarn
3. coordinate: grim, silent mansion; not coordinate: huge stone mansion
4. coordinate: tall, skinny, red-headed friend; not coordinate: wonderful old friend

Enrichment: Film Versions of Edgar Allan Poe Stories, p. 68

Suggested Responses

Students' scripts should reflect their notes on descriptions of setting, characters, camera shots, and special visual and sound effects.

Selection Test A, p. 69

Critical Reading

1. ANS: B	DIF: Easy	OBJ: Literary Analysis
2. ANS: C	DIF: Easy	OBJ: Reading Strategy
3. ANS: C	DIF: Easy	OBJ: Comprehension
4. ANS: B	DIF: Easy	OBJ: Literary Analysis
5. ANS: D	DIF: Easy	OBJ: Reading Strategy
6. ANS: D	DIF: Easy	OBJ: Literary Analysis
7. ANS: B	DIF: Easy	OBJ: Comprehension
8. ANS: B	DIF: Easy	OBJ: Interpretation

Vocabulary and Grammar

9. ANS: B	DIF: Easy	OBJ: Vocabulary
10. ANS: D	DIF: Easy	OBJ: Grammar

Essay

11. Students' essays should reflect the realization that both the owners and the house are dying or decaying. Madeline is dying of a disease. Roderick is dying of fear and torment. He is no longer a part of the living world but

only of his fantasies. The house is decaying because it has not been kept up. Students may even suggest that the siblings and the house are parts of the same reality, so that when Roderick and Madeline die, the house dies with them.

Difficulty: *Easy*
Objective: *Essay*

12. Students' essays should reflect that in this poem, the bird is not a symbol of hope, freedom, or light. It is a symbol of darkness, of the loss of hope. The raven symbolizes the poet's refusal to accept the death of Lenore, the woman he loved. Some students may suggest that the raven represents the part of the poet that knows the truth but will not accept it.

Difficulty: *Easy*
Objective: *Essay*

Selection Test B, p. 72

Critical Reading

1. ANS: C	DIF: Easy	OBJ: Literary Analysis
2. ANS: D	DIF: Average	OBJ: Comprehension
3. ANS: A	DIF: Average	OBJ: Interpretation
4. ANS: A	DIF: Easy	OBJ: Literary Analysis
5. ANS: D	DIF: Easy	OBJ: Reading Strategy
6. ANS: C	DIF: Average	OBJ: Interpretation
7. ANS: B	DIF: Challenging	OBJ: Comprehension
8. ANS: A	DIF: Challenging	OBJ: Interpretation
9. ANS: B	DIF: Easy	OBJ: Comprehension
10. ANS: D	DIF: Easy	OBJ: Interpretation
11. ANS: A	DIF: Average	OBJ: Literary Analysis
12. ANS: D	DIF: Challenging	OBJ: Interpretation
13. ANS: C	DIF: Average	OBJ: Reading Strategy

Vocabulary and Grammar

14. ANS: D	DIF: Average	OBJ: Vocabulary
15. ANS: B	DIF: Easy	OBJ: Vocabulary
16. ANS: D	DIF: Challenging	OBJ: Vocabulary
17. ANS: C	DIF: Easy	OBJ: Grammar

Essay

18. Students might mention feelings such as surprise, fear, dislike, curiosity, or even pleasure in their encounter with the raven. They may say that they would respond to the raven less dramatically and more scientifically than the speaker does. They might take the bird's appearance less personally. They may be less likely to see it as a supernatural messenger and may suggest that the word "Nevermore" has no real significance and is simply the only word it learned from a former master.

Difficulty: *Easy*

Objective: *Essay*

19. Students who agree with this interpretation should note that just about everything Usher does is unrelated to any existence outside his house or mind. They should mention such things as Usher's strange creations in all area of art, especially his abstract paintings; the painful acuteness of his senses; and his absorption in fantasy literature. Students who disagree may say that Usher represents anyone completely isolated from others, not just a creative artist. Some students may point to Usher's affluence, rather than his creativity, as the root of his problem. They may cite evidence such as his large estate, servants, and lack of gainful employment to suggest that wealth and privilege without purpose may be destructive. Some students may see in Usher a member of a doomed family whose weaknesses through several generations lead to destruction, or they may place more emphasis on supernatural causes, such as a family curse, as the root of his problems.

Difficulty: *Average*
Objective: *Essay*

"The Minister's Black Veil"
Nathaniel Hawthorne

Vocabulary Warm-up Exercises, p. 76

A.
1. apprehensive
2. averse
3. intellect
4. instinctive
5. iniquity
6. amiss
7. ostentatious
8. refrain

B. Sample Answers

1. Meg was charmed by Ben's <u>amiable</u> behavior.
2. Mike's greatest <u>attribute</u> was loyalty, which was deeply ingrained in his personality.
3. Before punishing him, the principal made remarks in <u>censure</u> of Jay's conduct.
4. Inez did an <u>energetic</u> workout, performing her routines rapidly and enthusiastically.
5. Through the telescope on a clear night, we could see a <u>multitude</u> of twinkling stars.
6. The dog had a <u>placid</u> disposition, lying quietly and appearing to smile at visitors.
7. Mr. Lindgren <u>retained</u> a large part of his fortune, giving only a little money to charity.
8. A <u>venerable</u> advisor has given reliable counsel for many years.

Reading Warm-up A, p. 77

Sample Answers

1. and fearful; The opposite of *apprehensive* is *confident* or *fearless*.

2. (has indulged in sin and . . . he is tormented with pains in both body and soul); *virtue*

3. but he has behaved . . . and has lost all his money; *correct, accurate*

4. *showy, flashy;* Paul was *ostentatious* in his taste, favoring brightly colored ties and jackets.

5. (hardly . . . to recovering their lost youth); *opposed to*

6. uttered again and again; repeated

7. (rivalries got the better of them); *instinct*

8. because the Fountain of Youth is a product of myth, not science; *mind*

Reading Warm-up B, p. 78

Sample Answers

1. one of those ancient bits of wisdom that everyone accepted; *elderly, ancient, aged*

2. (Marcy had . . . a strong doubt . . . you would find just the opposite); Even after listening to Tad's explanation, I *retained* some doubts about his honesty.

3. became an . . . of a person's identity; *characteristic; trait*

4. the head cheerleader, a peppy . . . girl; *listless, lethargic*

5. (disapproval, even . . ., as if clothes could pose a threat . . .); *praise*

6. (blend in with the . . . of the crowd); After the interesting lecture, excited audience members posed a *multitude* of questions.

7. who valued quiet thoughtfulness; *quiet, tranquil, peaceful, calm*

8. encouraging smile; The opposite of *amiable* is *unfriendly* or *hostile*.

Literary Analysis: Parable, p. 79

Sample Responses

1. The simple description of the villagers sounds like people everywhere: The children behave like most children, the bachelors behave like most bachelors.

2. No name is given to the deceased. The point is not *who* the deceased was, but the way that the other people responded to her death.

3. The language of this excerpt focuses on the veil and speaks of it in strong and symbolic language.

Reading Strategy: Draw Inferences About Meaning, p. 80

Possible Responses

1. Students may know that wearing a veil like this is not normal, and that a minister is assumed to be close to God. As a result, students may infer that the veil represents a division between Hooper and God.

2. Students will probably understand how busybodies like to interfere with other people's lives. As a result, they may infer that something very significant has happened to make Hooper different and unapproachable about the veil.

Vocabulary Builder, p. 81

A. Sample Responses

1. They are equal.
2. It divides the earth into two equal halves.
3. equality under the law; equal payments or punishments
4. They are equal.
5. tightrope walker; must maintain balance, distributing weight equally as he or she carefully walks the tightrope

B. 1. E; 2. J; 3. F; 4. G; 5. C; 6. I; 7. A; 8. D; 9. B; 10. H

Grammar and Style: Varying Sentence Openers, p. 82

A. Wordings of responses will vary, but students should recognize that the first sentence opens with a prepositional phrase *(after a brief interval)* and also uses inverted order, placing the subject *(Mr. Hooper)* after the verb *(came)*. The second sentence opens with a participial phrase *(turning his veiled face from one group to another)*. The third sentence opens in the usual way, with the subject (the indefinite pronoun *Such*).

B. Sample Response

Into the room where the corpse was laid stepped the clergyman. He bent over the coffin to take a last farewell of his deceased parishioner. As he stooped, his veil hung straight down from his forehead. The dead maiden's eyes were closed forever; otherwise she might have seen his face. Seeming to fear her glance nevertheless, Mr. Hooper hastily caught back the black veil.

Enrichment: Art, p. 85

Sample Responses

1. The colors of the painting are neutral—gray-blue, black, gray, dark brown, yellow beige. They are not joyful colors. The people are dressed mainly in dark colors. The contrasting whiteness of the snow adds no warmth and little light to the painting—everything seems dark and washed out. The mood produced by this lack of color is somber and sad, harsh and unforgiving, very much like the mood of the story.

2. A wintry scene is appropriate to the text because the events that Hawthorne narrates have a darkness, emotional coldness, and starkness about them that seems wintry. The characters seem imprisoned in the grip of a spiritual terror and isolation that suggests winter with no possibility of spring.

3. The light background of the snow makes everything seem darker in hue, just as the minister's veil drains life and color from everything that it confronts. The white door of the church, with its contrasting black window above, repeats the snowy, bleak landscape of the whole

picture rather than inviting the viewer to a warm and cheerful interior. The same is true of the white curtains in the black windows of the houses. Nothing in this painting suggests cheer.

4. The church dominates the landscape of the picture, as it does the setting of the story, but it is set to one side. The wintry track of the road takes center stage and fades to nothing at the horizon. The trees are lifeless. There is a lack of hope here. In a similar way, Hawthorne's tale seems to suggest a lack of hope for human lives. Although some of the people are grouped in the picture, there is a separateness about them. We don't know how the groups relate to each other or how the individuals in each group do. The fence in the foreground also hints at separation. Perhaps the most arresting figure is that near the center of the picture. It is solitary and silhouetted—utterly alone. As in the story, the picture seems to stress our separation from, and lack of knowledge about, each other.

5. The painting is an appropriate accompaniment to the story in the importance that it puts on religion, as shown by the church. It also reflects the themes of human isolation and lack of hope that are found in the story. Its chilling bleakness is similarly appropriate.

Selection Test A, p. 86

Critical Reading

1. ANS: C	DIF: Easy	OBJ: Literary Analysis
2. ANS: B	DIF: Easy	OBJ: Interpretation
3. ANS: D	DIF: Easy	OBJ: Reading Strategy
4. ANS: A	DIF: Easy	OBJ: Reading Strategy
5. ANS: C	DIF: Easy	OBJ: Interpretation
6. ANS: C	DIF: Easy	OBJ: Comprehension
7. ANS: D	DIF: Easy	OBJ: Literary Analysis
8. ANS: B	DIF: Easy	OBJ: Literary Analysis

Vocabulary and Grammar

9. ANS: B	DIF: Easy	OBJ: Vocabulary
10. ANS: D	DIF: Easy	OBJ: Grammar

Essay

11. Students' essays should reflect that according to the story, dying sinners are changed because of the example of the minister and his black veil. However, the other members of the parish, including his own beloved fiancée, are isolated from him, either through fear, lack of understanding, or general uneasiness. In these cases, people may have been less likely to listen to his sermons and other religious statements. They may have been less likely to accept his religious teachings. So perhaps his wearing of the veil is a powerful statement but does not have the effect he wishes.

Difficulty: *Easy*
Objective: *Essay*

12. Some students may suggest that the minister is confronting the people at his deathbed by asking them why they are so fearful of the black veil he wears. Don't they understand that they all wear black veils, too? He suggests that they are as sinful or as hopeful of hiding their shame as he is. In asking these questions, he may be admitting that his lifelong wearing of the veil has been unsuccessful, since his parishioners do not understand his message that with or without a physical veil, they are all still sinners.

Difficulty: *Easy*
Objective: *Essay*

Selection Test B, p. 89

Critical Reading

1. ANS: B	DIF: Average	OBJ: Comprehension
2. ANS: D	DIF: Easy	OBJ: Comprehension
3. ANS: C	DIF: Average	OBJ: Interpretation
4. ANS: D	DIF: Easy	OBJ: Literary Analysis
5. ANS: C	DIF: Challenging	OBJ: Literary Analysis
6. ANS: A	DIF: Average	OBJ: Literary Analysis
7. ANS: B	DIF: Challenging	OBJ: Literary Analysis
8. ANS: C	DIF: Average	OBJ: Literary Analysis
9. ANS: B	DIF: Average	OBJ: Interpretation
10. ANS: C	DIF: Average	OBJ: Reading Strategy
11. ANS: D	DIF: Average	OBJ: Reading Strategy

Vocabulary and Grammar

12. ANS: A	DIF: Easy	OBJ: Vocabulary
13. ANS: B	DIF: Average	OBJ: Vocabulary
14. ANS: B	DIF: Average	OBJ: Vocabulary
15. ANS: D	DIF: Easy	OBJ: Grammar

Essay

16. Some students may feel that Hooper's veil is confession of general wrongfulness stemming from the belief that all human-beings are sinners in the wake of the Fall of Man (original sin in the Garden of Eden) or is a confession of more specific wrongdoing, even of some particularly terrible sin, the details of which Mr. Hooper is hiding. Others may feel that he is making a statement and is less concerned with confessing his own sins than with giving his congregation a terrible reminder of their own sins, or of the belief that human beings are all sinners. Some students may say that the veil can function in both ways at the same time.

Difficulty: *Easy*
Objective: *Essay*

17. Students will probably recognize that Hawthorne's Puritans are close-knit in their small communities and that their lives center around the church, making the pastor an important figure. They are concerned with religion

and sin to a great degree. Some students may mention that Hawthorne is stressing the Puritans' hypocrisy, despite their concern with religion and sin. On the other hand, they may note that Hawthorne does make the Puritans seem human: they admire each other, they gossip, they celebrate happy events, the children make merry. Some students may feel that Hawthorne is fond of Hooper, whom he shows as a gentle soul; others may feel that he sees Hooper's veil as an extreme, even harmful gesture, and may mention his behavior toward Elizabeth as particularly extreme and cruel.

Difficulty: *Average*

Objective: *Essay*

18. Students should mention that objects need not be strange or unique in themselves to acquire symbolic power. Rather, they become symbolic because of their particular setting, the events of which they are a part, and the people who use them. So a veil on the bonnet of a woman may be purely decorative or may symbolize ornamentation or proper dress; a veil worn by a nun or a Moslem woman may symbolize purity or piety; a veil worn by a widow may symbolize grief. When such a veil is taken out of that common context and used in a more bizarre way, it becomes a potent symbol, with power beyond the ordinary to cause an emotional reaction in all who see it.

Difficulty: *Challenging*

Objective: *Essay*

Benchmark Test 3, p. 92

MULTIPLE CHOICE

1. ANS: C
2. ANS: B
3. ANS: A
4. ANS: A
5. ANS: A
6. ANS: D
7. ANS: C
8. ANS: B
9. ANS: A
10. ANS: D
11. ANS: A
12. ANS: B
13. ANS: B
14. ANS: B
15. ANS: D
16. ANS: D
17. ANS: D
18. ANS: A
19. ANS: B
20. ANS: C
21. ANS: A
22. ANS: C
23. ANS: B
24. ANS: A
25. ANS: C
26. ANS: A
27. ANS: C

Diagnostic Test 4, p. 98

MULTIPLE CHOICE

1. ANS: C
2. ANS: A
3. ANS: D
4. ANS: B
5. ANS: B
6. ANS: C
7. ANS: D
8. ANS: B
9. ANS: C
10. ANS: A
11. ANS: B
12. ANS: A
13. ANS: C
14. ANS: B
15. ANS: B

from *Moby-Dick* by Herman Melville

Vocabulary Warm-up Exercises, p. 102

A. 1. accumulated
2. cringing
3. outrageous
4. dislodged
5. foreboding
6. acquiescence
7. downcast
8. imperial

B. Sample Answers
1. F; *Admonitions* are warnings.
2. T; A *haughty* attitude might easily lead to arrogant behavior.
3. F; Heroism is related to virtue and courage, not to deceit.
4. T; An *inscrutable* person would be hard to analyze.
5. F; If you *intercept* a message, you are in possession of it.
6. T; *Pagan* means "heathen."
7. F; By definition, a *specific* argument is detailed and particular, not vague or general.
8. T; *Vengeance* involves retribution or retaliation.

Reading Warm-up A, p. 103

Sample Answers

1. <u>he had . . . such a record of good conduct</u>; Iris began to save three months ago, and by now she had <u>accumulated</u> a sizable reserve fund.
2. (. . . that his mother couldn't refuse . . . he finally got her . . . they made reservations); *agreement*
3. <u>gray and ominous . . . as if a violent storm might erupt . . .</u>; Greg was full of *foreboding*, feeling that something bad was about to happen.
4. (her . . . face showing her nervousness); *happy, cheerful*
5. (the boat . . . itself from the dock and set out for the open sea); The opposite of *dislodged* is *attached*.
6. <u>she was gripping the edge of her seat . . . with anxiety each time the boat went over even the smallest wave</u>; *shrinking*
7. (to go to all this trouble and not even see a tail or a fin); If your behavior in school is *outrageous*, you may be sent home for a few days.
8. <u>dominated the whole ocean . . . enormous power</u>; *figuratively*

Reading Warm-up B, p. 104

Sample Answers

1. <u>that had won fame in rough and challenging quests</u>; Dr. Martin Luther King, Jr. led a *heroic* campaign for social justice and equality of opportunity.
2. (mysterious); *obscure, incomprehensible*
3. <u>privateers . . . and damage British ships</u>; *interrupt*
4. <u>ignored British . . . to stop these raids</u>; Nathan didn't heed his parents' *admonitions* to dress warmly, and as a result he caught a cold on the ski trip.
5. (when the Americans ignored . . . the British sought . . . they burned New Bedford); *revenge, requital, retribution, retaliation*
6. <u>display of arrogance</u>; The opposite of *haughty* is *mild* or *humble*.
7. <u>detailed</u>; *vague, general*
8. (ruled by no caring divinity but by the hostile forces of nature)

Literary Analysis: Symbol, p. 105

Possible Responses

1. Starbuck may represent the voice of reason and religious faith; both are overridden by Ahab's obsession.
2. The sea may represent the overwhelming forces of nature that overpower humanity and its efforts, represented by the ship; the sea may represent Ahab's fanatical, irrational obsession (or fanaticism or obsessive behavior in general), which destroys human society or the spirit of community, represented by the ship.
3. The sky hawk may represent heavenly faith and innocence, which like the crew is destroyed by Ahab's fanatical, obsessive behavior.

Reading Strategy: Recognize Symbols, p. 106

Sample Responses

1. the "peculiar mark" of his walk, his "ribbed and dented brow" with its "still stranger footprints" of "his one unsleeping, ever-pacing thought"
2. thought; a warped nature; brooding; obsession; vengeance
3. his footprints; the imprints of his one good leg and one ivory peg
4. comparing the planks with those prints to geological stones; calling the mark of his walk "peculiar," connecting the imprints on the planks to the imprint on his mind "of his one unsleeping, ever-pacing thought" (of vengeance against the whale)
5. obsession; vengeance; Ahab's warped, obsessive nature

Vocabulary Builder, p. 107

A. 1. D; 2. B; 3. B; 4. A; 5. C
B. 1. D; 2. C; 3. A; 4. B

Grammar and Style: Agreement With Collective Nouns, p. 108

A. Students should underline the collective nouns and circle the correct verbs and pronouns.

1. collective noun: company; verb: are
2. collective noun: crew; verb: perform; pronoun: their
3. collective noun: crew; verb: disperses
4. collective noun: team; verb: was
5. collective noun: school; verb: breaks
6. collective noun: flock; verb: flies; pronoun: its

B. Sample Responses

1. A herd of whales was blocking the forward motion of the ship.
   The herd of whales were approaching the ship from several directions.
2. The committee meets on Thursdays at the public library.
   The committee have different occupations and schedules.
3. The jury decides whether the prisoner is innocent or guilty.
   The jury have voted according to their individual consciences.

Enrichment: Art, p. 111

Possible Responses

1. The picture reveals Ahab's inflexibility in his stance— legs spread apart, firmly bracing him, head lifted almost defiantly, gazing out over the sea. The shadow cast by Ahab strengthens the image. The shadow of his good leg forms a triangle with his legs, an additional brace. The shadows on his figure make it seem substantial and three-dimensional. Though his face is white, shadows define his hard, craggy features.

2. The feeling conveyed by the picture of Moby-Dick leaping from the sea is one of great, even frightening, power. Two-thirds of his body protrudes vertically from the water. The water from his mighty spout slashes across the picture, indicating rapid movement. He is truly fearsome—almost supernatural in his might—and triumphant. The white body of the whale adds to the effect of power. It is almost without shadows—only a few to mark its ear and "wrinkled brow." It is solid, reminding the viewer of "that wall, shoved near to me" that Ahab mentions. Moby-Dick's body contrasts totally with the sky and sea. It seems to be its own source of light, like the stars it appears to reach for. Like them, too, the whale is an overwhelming force of nature. The stars also help the viewer place Moby-Dick, showing that he has risen above the ocean's surface.

3. The picture of the whale and the boat expresses the insignificance of humans in the face of the brute force of nature. The variation in size is one way the picture makes this point. Only the huge tail of Moby-Dick is shown. The composition emphasizes that it is as long as a boat that holds several men. The men themselves are tiny in comparison. Flung high into midair along with their equipment, they are puny and helpless. The height of the boat above the tail is stark evidence of its power. Yet, there is something almost calm about the tail itself that contrasts with the chaos of the tossed boat. It suggests the ease with which natural forces can destroy the work of humans.

4. Some students might find the use of black and white appropriate because it would emphasize the stark power and opposition of the antagonists, Ahab and Moby-Dick. They may also see symbolism of good and evil in these colors. Students who like black-and-white illustrations may also mention the simplicity and clarity they give to the events and issues. Others may feel that full color makes the events seem more natural and adds reality to the complex events.

Selection Test A, p. 112

Critical Reading

1. ANS: B	DIF: Easy	OBJ: Comprehension
2. ANS: D	DIF: Easy	OBJ: Comprehension
3. ANS: B	DIF: Easy	OBJ: Literary Analysis
4. ANS: D	DIF: Easy	OBJ: Comprehension
5. ANS: A	DIF: Easy	OBJ: Reading Strategy
6. ANS: C	DIF: Easy	OBJ: Literary Analysis
7. ANS: C	DIF: Easy	OBJ: Literary Analysis
8. ANS: D	DIF: Easy	OBJ: Reading Strategy

Vocabulary and Grammar

9. ANS: B	DIF: Easy	OBJ: Vocabulary
10. ANS: C	DIF: Easy	OBJ: Grammar

Essay

11. Students may suggest that Ahab symbolizes the eternal struggle between humans and creatures, or humans and the natural world, or life and death, and so on. Accept any argument that a student can support with material from the selection.
Difficulty: *Easy*
Objective: *Essay*

12. Students' essays should reflect that in some ways, Ahab seems to be a free person. He has his own business, and he can sail wherever he likes. But students should also see that his obsession, which ultimately kills him, imprisons him even while he is alive. He can neither act nor think freely, because both his actions and thoughts are ruled by his feelings of vengeance and helplessness against a stronger rival.
Difficulty: *Easy*
Objective: *Essay*

Selection Test B, p. 115

Critical Reading

1. ANS: A	DIF: Easy	OBJ: Comprehension
2. ANS: C	DIF: Easy	OBJ: Comprehension
3. ANS: C	DIF: Average	OBJ: Comprehension
4. ANS: D	DIF: Easy	OBJ: Interpretation
5. ANS: B	DIF: Average	OBJ: Interpretation
6. ANS: D	DIF: Challenging	OBJ: Interpretation
7. ANS: C	DIF: Challenging	OBJ: Interpretation
8. ANS: A	DIF: Easy	OBJ: Reading Strategy
9. ANS: D	DIF: Challenging	OBJ: Reading Strategy
10. ANS: C	DIF: Easy	OBJ: Literary Analysis
11. ANS: C	DIF: Challenging	OBJ: Literary Analysis
12. ANS: A	DIF: Challenging	OBJ: Literary Analysis
13. ANS: B	DIF: Average	OBJ: Literary Analysis

Vocabulary and Grammar

14. ANS: D	DIF: Easy	OBJ: Vocabulary
15. ANS: A	DIF: Average	OBJ: Vocabulary
16. ANS: D	DIF: Average	OBJ: Grammar
17. ANS: C	DIF: Average	OBJ: Grammar

Essay

18. Ahab's good points could include the leadership ability that helps him unite and motivate the crew, his apparent liking and respect for his men, his generosity with money, and his physical bravery. Bad points should include his abandonment of the business of the voyage, his obsessive personality, and, most important, his willingness to endanger the lives of his crew to fulfill his own ends.
Difficulty: *Easy*

Objective: *Essay*

19. Students should recognize that these words apply well to Ahab. He is a ship's captain and thus at sea has a great deal of power with almost no external restraints. He also seems to lack the constraints that religious faith or fear of physical danger might provide. Thus there is nothing to keep him from being driven by his innermost necessities—hatred and vengefulness for Moby Dick. Students may even say that without external restraints, Ahab is a victim of his inner self. They may also see in Starbuck the opposite of Ahab: the external restraints of his position on the ship—he must obey Ahab—keep him from being driven by his inner recognition that Ahab's mission is wrong.

Difficulty: *Average*

Objective: *Essay*

20. Students may say that the scene is a good way of clarifying Ahab's motivation dramatically, through his own words and actions, rather than by having Ishmael merely summarize them. Students may also say that to make the idea of the mission against Moby-Dick believable, Melville had to show the great psychological power that Ahab exerts over his crew, whom he must persuade to give up their usual business and follow him, and without whose willing help Ahab cannot hope to succeed. In addition, the scene explores Ahab's obsession in his confrontation with Starbuck, tells us about reactions of some other characters to the quest and to Ahab, and establishes the reality of Moby-Dick outside the mind of Ahab. With its high drama and ritualistic events, the scene, despite clear elements foreshadowing, catches the reader up in Ahab's passion.

Difficulty: *Challenging*

Objective: *Essay*

from *Nature*, from *Self-Reliance*, "The Snowstorm," and "Concord Hymn"
Ralph Waldo Emerson

Vocabulary Warm-up Exercises, p. 119

A. 1. embattled
2. brink
3. melancholy
4. reside
5. misunderstood
6. testify
7. exhilaration
8. harmony

B. Sample Answers
1. Their habitual smiles showed us that our cousins had a <u>blithe</u> outlook on life.
2. Otis was not afraid to <u>contradict</u> the boss, saying that he completely disagreed with her.
3. Mark served as a <u>courier</u>, delivering the package promptly.

4. Hercules, a hero of ancient myth, was thought to be <u>immortal</u>, living forever with the gods.
5. Sam gladly <u>imparted</u> the news, revealing every detail of the story.
6. Known for her <u>integrity</u>, Mayor Zeiss has never faced a corruption inquiry.
7. If an event is described as an <u>occurrence</u>, it has definitely happened.
8. The sea seemed <u>tranquil</u>, with gentle waves lapping the shoreline.

Reading Warm-up A, p. 120

Sample Answers
1. <u>by gangs and street crime</u>; Because her boss was always frowning and ill-tempered with her, Cindy felt *embattled* at work.
2. (. . . about the poverty surrounding her . . .); The opposite of *melancholy* is *cheerfulness* or *happiness.*
3. <u>just a few days away from losing their apartment or their job</u>; *edge, verge*
4. <u>as if to be poor meant that you must also be a criminal</u>; *misinterpreted*
5. (the rich and the poor together, instead of separated); *strife, discord*
6. (it would not matter where you lived . . . a place where people could . . . in safety); *residence, residential*
7. *bear witness;* The defendant refused to take the stand at the trial, preferring that other witnesses *testify* in his favor.
8. <u>joy</u>; The opposite of *exhilaration* is *sadness, depression,* or *melancholy.*

Reading Warm-up B, p. 121

Sample Answers
1. <u>majority opinions</u>; *deny, oppose*
2. (peaceful); *stormy, turbulent*
3. <u>an utterly honest goal</u>; The opposite of *integrity* is *dishonesty* or *corruption.*
4. <u>or natural event</u>; We were eager to witness the launch of the first space shuttle, a landmark *occurrence.*
5. (brought messages from the outside world); *messenger*
6. (shared his experiences); On his visit, Craig *imparted* to us the latest news from the big city.
7. <u>combine thinkers and workers in . . . and peaceful harmony</u>; *anxious, unhappy*
8. <u>Brook Farm itself was hardly . . . . but its name lives on</u>; *deathless, undying, eternal*

Literary Analysis: Transcendentalism, p. 122

1. B; 2. C; 3. B; 4. B; 5. A; 6. A; 7. A

Reading Strategy: Challenge the Text, p. 123

Sample Responses

1. Society is the enemy of individualism; society forces people to conform.

2. Students should recognize that, following the opening sentence of the paragraph, the next three sentences constitute evidence. They will probably feel that these sentences do not offer strong support because they consist merely of additional assertions and are basically restatements of the opening assertion in different words.

3. Support: laws that limit freedoms; peer pressure to conform

   Refute: laws that protect freedoms; notice and sometimes admiration given those who are different

Vocabulary Builder, p. 124

A. Sample Responses

1. shining out in rays, or as if in rays
2. a line coming from the center of a circle like the spoke of a wheel
3. a heating device sending out rays of heat
4. an appliance that sends out or picks up messages broadcast like rays through the air, or air waves
5. emitting energy in waves or rays

B. 1. A; 2. D; 3. C; 4. B; 5. A; 6. B; 7. C; 8. D; 9. C; 10. B

Grammar and Style: Varying Sentence Length, p. 125

A. 1. A; 2. B

B. Sample Response

On April 19, 1775, a group of American farmers serving as Minute Men fired at the British at Lexington and Concord, Massachusetts. The American Revolution had begun. In his "Concord Hymn," sung on April 19, 1836, at the unveiling of a monument honoring the Minute Men's stand, Ralph Waldo Emerson described the first shot of the Revolution as "the shot heard round the world."

Enrichment: Local Landmarks p. 128

Suggested Responses

Students should provide clear and detailed answers. If students are having trouble finding a monument, suggest that they consult a local library or a historical society in the area.

Selection Test A, p. 129

Critical Reading

1. ANS: A	DIF: Easy	OBJ: Reading Strategy
2. ANS: B	DIF: Easy	OBJ: Literary Analysis
3. ANS: B	DIF: Easy	OBJ: Interpretation
4. ANS: C	DIF: Easy	OBJ: Interpretation
5. ANS: C	DIF: Easy	OBJ: Literary Analysis

6. ANS: C	DIF: Easy	OBJ: Interpretation
7. ANS: D	DIF: Easy	OBJ: Literary Analysis
8. ANS: B	DIF: Easy	OBJ: Literary Analysis

Vocabulary and Grammar

9. ANS: C	DIF: Easy	OBJ: Vocabulary
10. ANS: D	DIF: Easy	OBJ: Grammar

Essay

11. Students' essays should reflect that Emerson does not respect the expectations of society. He calls it a "conspiracy" against its members. He says it is a "joint-stock company," which expects each shareholder to give up his independence and individuality in order to prosper. He is against conformity and consistency, and recommends that people contradict themselves regularly if they believe different things on different days.

    Difficulty: *Easy*

    Objective: *Essay*

12. Students' essays should reflect that Emerson gives the wind of the snowstorm a human character—that of an architect blowing and shaping the earth through wind and snow. Throughout the storm, the wind creature affects the roofs, trees, doors, and coops, and changes their appearance overnight, in the same way that people build cities over many years.

    Difficulty: *Easy*

    Objective: *Essay*

Selection Test B, p. 132

Critical Reading

1. ANS: C	DIF: Challenging	OBJ: Literary Analysis
2. ANS: B	DIF: Easy	OBJ: Comprehension
3. ANS: C	DIF: Easy	OBJ: Reading Strategy
4. ANS: D	DIF: Average	OBJ: Literary Analysis
5. ANS: A	DIF: Average	OBJ: Reading Strategy
6. ANS: D	DIF: Average	OBJ: Comprehension
7. ANS: A	DIF: Average	OBJ: Literary Analysis
8. ANS: B	DIF: Average	OBJ: Interpretation
9. ANS: D	DIF: Average	OBJ: Interpretation
10. ANS: B	DIF: Easy	OBJ: Literary Analysis
11. ANS: A	DIF: Average	OBJ: Interpretation
12. ANS: C	DIF: Challenging	OBJ: Interpretation
13. ANS: D	DIF: Average	OBJ: Reading Strategy

Vocabulary and Grammar

14. ANS: D	DIF: Average	OBJ: Vocabulary
15. ANS: B	DIF: Average	OBJ: Grammar
16. ANS: B	DIF: Average	OBJ: Vocabulary
17. ANS: A	DIF: Easy	OBJ: Vocabulary

Essay

18. Students should cite or summarize lines from *Nature* that focus on the relationship between nature and the human spirit; for example, "In the woods is perpetual youth. Within these plantations of God, a decorum and sanctity reign"; "Standing on the bare ground—my head bathed by the blithe air and uplifted into infinite space—all mean egotism vanishes. I become a transparent eyeball: I am nothing: I see all: the currents of the Universal Being circulate through me: I am part or parcel of God"; and "Nature always wears the colors of the spirit."

Difficulty: *Easy*

Objective: *Essay*

19. "The shot heard round the world" underscores patriotism and the American struggle for liberty as a model for the world. Students who feel these quotations contradict each other may say that the quotation from Nature criticizes nationalism and hence patriotism. Students who feel that they do not contradict each other may say that both place great value on freedom and independence.

Difficulty: *Average*

Objective: *Essay*

20. Students who feel that the two beliefs have an inherent conflict may focus on the tension between the self-reliant individual and the spiritual community. Those who feel there is no real conflict may say that Emerson stresses that one must be an independent, self-reliant individual to reach the spiritual heights of the Over-Soul and that the individual is in conflict only with society on a more material plane.

Difficulty: *Challenging*

Objective: *Essay*

From the Scholar's Desk

Gretel Ehrlich Introduces from *Walden* by Henry David Thoreau, p. 135

1. She grew up on the central California coast.
2. Examples include Thoreau's opinions about land and home ownership, about the relative importance of wealth or poverty, and about life lived on a moment-by-moment basis.
3. A. Details include the changing weather, changing human relationships, physical changes in our bodies, and the cycle of natural change.
   B. Sample responses: Yes, because nature is always developing, growing, and changing; no, because human beings ought to hold onto certain fundamental principles that do not change.
4. Thoreau would have us simplify, slow down, become quiet, and try to reach the heart of things.
5. He means the fresh, dawn-like character of things—in other words, their essence in the here and now.

6. Sample responses: Yes, because our individuality is our most precious asset; no, because cooperation, harmony, and interdependence are sometimes essential.
7. Sample questions: Was Thoreau ever apprehensive or agitated when he was living at Walden Pond? What happened to Thoreau after his stay at Walden Pond was over?

Gretel Ehrlich

Listening and Viewing, p. 136

Segment 1: Gretel Ehrlich believes that coming from super-materialistic America we may not have a concept of what other people are like. Traveling provides insight into the way others live and deal with hardships and, most importantly, helps an individual develop compassion. Students may suggest that these experiences afforded them opportunities to learn about different people and places and gain a new understanding of humanity.

Segment 2: Gretel Ehrlich structured her book that describes her experiences in Greenland like Thoreau's *Walden:* the book chronicles the writer's experiences during the four seasons. Ehrlich also lived off of the land in Greenland and Wyoming for many years, much the way Thoreau lived close to nature at Walden Pond.

Segment 3: Gretel Ehrlich thinks that writing is a fresh rendition of an experience, character, or observation; it is crucial to take notes in order to have details to expand into a story. Students may say they use scraps of paper, notebooks, journals, outlines, computers, etc.

Segment 4: Gretel Ehrlich believes that the writer must contribute something to society that is worth reading and has universal appeal and value. Students may suggest that by reading anthropological books they would appreciate the common bonds of humanity and learn to tolerate the differences.

from *Walden* and from *Civil Disobedience* by Henry David Thoreau

Vocabulary Warm-up Exercises, p. 138

A. 1. cluttered
2. essentially
3. external
4. premises
5. superfluous
6. calculation
7. anticipated
8. enterprises

B. Sample Answers
1. F; Someone acting in *conformity* would be considered conventional.
2. F; *Inherent* means "innate" or "inborn," so something *inherent* would not be superficial.
3. T; Commuter trains are a means or method of public transportation.

4. F; *Piety* means "devotion."

5. F; *Restricted* means "limited" or "curbed," not "increased" or "enhanced."

6. T; A clever lie could have the appearance or simulation of truth.

7. F; *Shun* means "to avoid."

8. F; *Transmit* means "to send, convey, or pass along."

Reading Warm-up A, p. 139

Sample Answers

1. at the school gym . . . to enter the . . . hikers had to bring with them a backpack; A sign clearly stated that it was illegal to distribute flyers on the *premises*.

2. (how difficult it would be); *expected, forecast, predicted*

3. such a heavy pack . . . take everything out and start from scratch; *crowded, congested*

4. (anything you don't need); The opposite of *superfluous* is *necessary, required,* or *essential*.

5. (on this trip . . . it would not be one of those fun-filled . . . he was used to); *undertakings, ventures*

6. that showed how much weight you could carry on your back, according to how much you weighed; *precise*

7. (rain, snow, hail: all the . . . elements that can seep into your skin and your pack); The opposite of *external* is *internal*.

8. . . . learned that . . . the less you brought, the better; *Numismatics* may be defined, *essentially*, as the study of coins.

Reading Warm-up B, p. 140

Sample Answers

1. duty of human beings; Each person has an *inherent* right to equal protection under the law.

2. (to resist . . . keep pace with his companions . . . he hears a different drummer); *conform*

3. approach or . . .; *manner, way*

4. or limited; *increased, enlarged, augmented*

5. (directly . . . a set of beliefs to two of the most important men of the twentieth century); *convey, pass along, send*

6. shade or; *appearance*

7. staying away from their jobs in a massive general strike; The opposite of *shun* is *accept* or *embrace*.

8. (with a reverence that bordered on); *pious*

Literary Analysis: Style, p. 141

Sample Responses

1. Word choice: Thoreau uses fairly simple words sprinkled with an occasionally complex, formal term, such as *auroral, terrestrial, celestial.*

2. Sentence length: Thoreau uses fairly long sentences in this passage.

3. Sentence type/structure: Thoreau tends to use long simple or compound sentences lengthened by several verbal and prepositional phrases. He varies sentence

beginnings by opening one sentence with a prepositional phrase.

4. Rhythm: Thoreau achieves a quiet, regular rhythm in this descriptive passage.

5. Literary devices: Thoreau uses fairly vivid images and figurative language, such as "airy and unplastered cabin," "broken strains . . . of terrestrial music"; and the comparison of the cabin to a place "where a goddess might trail her garments."

Reading Strategy: Evaluate the Writer's Statement of Philosophy, p. 142

Students may cite some of the following main ideas: Simplify your own life and concentrate on what is truly meaningful. Value your own life, no matter how poor it may seem. Dare to be a nonconformist. Be wary lest you serve only the needs of the few. Use civil disobedience, if necessary, to make your government more responsive to individual needs.

Students should cite or summarize different portions of the selections to support each main idea and then list personal experiences that support or refute the main idea. Evaluations of each main idea should take into account students' personal experiences.

Vocabulary Builder, p. 143

A. 1. C; 2. A; 3. A

B. 1. A; 2. C; 3. B; 4. C; 5. B; 6. A; 7. B; 8. B

Grammar and Style: Infinitives and Infinitive Phrases, p. 144

A. Students should underline infinitive phrases.

1. n, to live deliberately

2. n, to ponder only the essential facts of life

3. adj, to live

B. Sample Responses

1. Thoreau wanted to live simply.

2. He follows the Transcendentalist teaching to make a friend of nature.

3. Thoreau advises individuals to heed the sound of a different drummer.

Enrichment: Social Studies, p. 147

Sample Responses

1. O; 2. O; 3. O; 4. S; 5. S; 6. S

Students should support their answers with details from the selections.

Selection Test A, p. 148

Critical Reading

1. ANS: B	DIF: Easy	OBJ: Comprehension
2. ANS: B	DIF: Easy	OBJ: Reading Strategy
3. ANS: D	DIF: Easy	OBJ: Literary Analysis
4. ANS: C	DIF: Easy	OBJ: Literary Analysis

5. ANS: C	DIF: Easy	OBJ: Reading Strategy
6. ANS: C	DIF: Easy	OBJ: Comprehension
7. ANS: A	DIF: Easy	OBJ: Comprehension
8. ANS: C	DIF: Easy	OBJ: Reading Strategy

Vocabulary and Grammar

9. ANS: B	DIF: Easy	OBJ: Vocabulary
10. ANS: A	DIF: Easy	OBJ: Grammar

Essay

11. Students' essays should reflect that Thoreau seems to be saying that too much time spent in one activity or way of life does not lead to greater skill or understanding but only to unthinking habit. He apparently thinks that people should attempt to learn from different ways of life, or different occupations. Some students may remember that Thoreau says earlier in the selection that he went to the woods because he wished to live "deliberately," meaning with a purpose. Now, he says he left the woods for the same reason. He wants to explore other ideas and actions.

Difficulty: *Easy*

Objective: *Essay*

12. Students' essays should reflect that Thoreau believes in the saying, "That government is best which governs least." He believes that governments get in the way of people behaving in socially useful ways. He blames the Mexican war on the actions of a few people, and says the majority of the people do not want the war. He believes governments find it easy to convince people that they need a government. Thoreau's beliefs support the actions of people, not governments.

Difficulty: *Easy*

Objective: *Essay*

Selection Test B, p. 153

Critical Reading

1. ANS: D	DIF: Average	OBJ: Reading Strategy
2. ANS: B	DIF: Average	OBJ: Reading Strategy
3. ANS: A	DIF: Challenging	OBJ: Comprehension
4. ANS: A	DIF: Average	OBJ: Literary Analysis
5. ANS: D	DIF: Challenging	OBJ: Literary Analysis
6. ANS: B	DIF: Average	OBJ: Interpretation
7. ANS: C	DIF: Challenging	OBJ: Interpretation
8. ANS: A	DIF: Average	OBJ: Interpretation
9. ANS: D	DIF: Average	OBJ: Reading Strategy
10. ANS: C	DIF: Easy	OBJ: Interpretation
11. ANS: C	DIF: Average	OBJ: Comprehension
12. ANS: B	DIF: Challenging	OBJ: Literary Analysis
13. ANS: D	DIF: Average	OBJ: Reading Strategy

14. ANS: A	DIF: Challenging	OBJ: Reading Strategy

Vocabulary and Grammar

15. ANS: B	DIF: Easy	OBJ: Vocabulary
16. ANS: B	DIF: Average	OBJ: Grammar
17. ANS: C	DIF: Average	OBJ: Vocabulary

Essay

18. Students should recognize that by moving to the woods, Thoreau was able to simplify his life, thereby allowing himself to concentrate on what he considered the important things involving the human spirit; he also lived closer to nature and gained a keener appreciation of its beauty and power. Among the details students may cite are the details about the poet appreciating a farm more than a farmer does; the descriptions of the Hollowell farm; the paragraph beginning "I went to the woods because I wished to live deliberately"; all the elaboration, in the next paragraph, on the idea of "Simplicity, simplicity, simplicity!"; and the details in the paragraph beginning "However mean your life is, meet it and live it."

Difficulty: *Easy*

Objective: *Essay*

19. Students should recognize that by taking action, Thoreau does not mean that people need to be busy, but that they need to contemplate the essentials of nature and the human spirit. Students may suggest that taking action can involve expressing one's opinion, refusing to go along with the rest of society, and/or dedicating oneself to a simple life experiencing nature and the human spirit. The many references to time stress Thoreau's idea that life is precious. It seems Thoreau is urging people to take action immediately, not to wait.

Difficulty: *Challenging*

Objective: *Essay*

Emily Dickinson's Poetry

Vocabulary Warm-up Exercises, p. 155

A. 1. leisure
   2. absorb
   3. portion
   4. assignable
   5. keepsakes
   6. quivering
   7. onset
   8. wrung

B. Sample Answers

   1. Two setbacks <u>befell</u> James, but he dealt with them well.
   2. Because our resources are <u>finite</u>, we must limit our pledge of money for that cause.

3. The <u>immortality</u> of the Greek gods was one way in which they differed from humans.

4. The election was close, and the winner received a very small <u>majority</u> of votes.

5. In all his undertakings, Tom <u>strove</u> hard, putting in maximum effort.

6. Willing to use an educated guess, Phil <u>surmised</u> the ending from hints in the story.

7. In favor of exhibiting the new painting, the museum director prepared to <u>unveil</u> it.

8. <u>Valves</u> are used to regulate the flow of water in those pipes.

Reading Warm-up A, p. 156

Sample Answers

1. <u>often finished her homework early . . . she had an hour or two of . . . before dinner</u>; When Rita had *leisure*, she enjoyed reading Victorian novels.

2. (usually fairy tales that left Betsy . . . with delight); *shaking*

3. <u>reserved a . . . of each journal page . . . fill this section</u>; *part*

4. (. . . she'd accumulated); *assimilate, take in, accumulate*

5. (each fictional character . . . to a poem . . . she might use the character in a story poem . . . lyric poem using the character as the speaker); *assign, assignment*

6. <u>late fall, with the . . . of winter not far off</u>; *approach, beginning*

7. (had survived and were treasured in the family as); I treasured the *keepsakes* that Grandpa had left me in his will.

8. <u>a difficult time when Hetty had . . . beautiful verse out of the challenge of her life experience</u>; *squeezed, compressed*

Reading Warm-up B, p. 157

Sample Answers

1. <u>to create a distinctive style . . . in this effort</u>; Spending hours at the piano daily, Ian *strove* to refine his technique.

2. (it is the use of surprise . . . there are very few Dickinson poems); The opposite of *majority* is *minority*.

3. <u>or inferred</u>; *guessed*

4. <u>surprising word choices . . . mechanical devices, as if the soul had water spigots or faucets . . .</u>

5. (we learn that death . . . the speaker before the poem opens); *happened to*

6. <u>the perspective of someone approaching the threshold of . . .</u>; The opposite of *immortality* is *death* or *mortality*.

7. <u>or limited</u>; *restricted, bounded, limited*

8. (or reveal); *hide, conceal*

Literary Analysis: Slant Rhyme, p. 158

1. see/me, exact; 2. chill/Tulle, slant; 3. Despair/Air, exact; 4. privacy/Infinity, slant

Reading Strategy: Analyze Images, p. 159

Sample Responses

1. The image of the soul shutting the door, which appeals to the senses of both sound and sight, helps us visualize the privacy of the soul and understand the abruptness with which it shuts out the world.

2. The images of the chariots at the low gate and the emperor kneeling upon the mat, which appeal to the senses of sight and touch, help us understand the soul's in difference to even the magnificent and powerful.

Vocabulary Builder, p. 160

A. Sample Responses

1. to limit a word to a particular meaning; to provide the limits of a word's meaning

2. to redo the outer limits, or outside, of something (such as a piece of furniture)

3. ending (as of a piece of music)

B. 1. surmised; 2. infinity; 3. oppresses; 4. finite; 5. cornice

C. 1. C; 2. D; 3. B; 4. B

Grammar and Style: Gerunds, p. 161

A. Students should circle the gerunds.

1. S, talking; 2. OP, dancing; 3. DO, swimming; 4. PA, running; 5. OP, cooking

B. Students' sentences will vary but should use the words as subjects, direct objects, predicate nominatives, and objects of prepositions.

Enrichment: Art, p. 164

Suggested Responses

Students should demonstrate understanding of the images in the poems and the way in which the paintings relate to Dickinson's messages and themes.

Selection Test A, p. 165

Critical Reading

1. ANS: D	DIF: Easy	OBJ: Comprehension
2. ANS: C	DIF: Easy	OBJ: Reading Strategy
3. ANS: D	DIF: Easy	OBJ: Literary Analysis
4. ANS: B	DIF: Easy	OBJ: Reading Strategy
5. ANS: C	DIF: Easy	OBJ: Literary Analysis
6. ANS: C	DIF: Easy	OBJ: Reading Strategy
7. ANS: C	DIF: Easy	OBJ: Literary Analysis
8. ANS: A	DIF: Easy	OBJ: Interpretation

Vocabulary and Grammar

9. ANS: A	DIF: Easy	OBJ: Vocabulary
10. ANS: A	DIF: Easy	OBJ: Grammar

Essay

11. Students' essays should reflect that Emily Dickinson wrote poems that showed she did not fear death. The image of a dressy gown may suggest that she thought she should dress up for an event as important as death, or that she felt that going to one's death was as important as going to a fancy event.

    Difficulty: *Easy*

    Objective: *Essay*

12. Accept any poem that uses opposites in the way they are used in Dickinson's poem.

    Difficulty: *Easy*

    Objective: *Essay*

Selection Test B, p. 168

Critical Reading

1. ANS: C	DIF: Average	OBJ: Comprehension
2. ANS: B	DIF: Easy	OBJ: Literary Analysis
3. ANS: A	DIF: Easy	OBJ: Reading Strategy
4. ANS: A	DIF: Average	OBJ: Interpretation
5. ANS: C	DIF: Challenging	OBJ: Interpretation
6. ANS: C	DIF: Challenging	OBJ: Literary Analysis
7. ANS: C	DIF: Average	OBJ: Comprehension
8. ANS: A	DIF: Easy	OBJ: Reading Strategy
9. ANS: B	DIF: Challenging	OBJ: Comprehension
10. ANS: B	DIF: Average	OBJ: Reading Strategy
11. ANS: A	DIF: Easy	OBJ: Literary Analysis
12. ANS: C	DIF: Challenging	OBJ: Reading Strategy
13. ANS: D	DIF: Average	OBJ: Interpretation

Vocabulary and Grammar

14. ANS: A	DIF: Easy	OBJ: Vocabulary
15. ANS: B	DIF: Easy	OBJ: Vocabulary
16. ANS: D	DIF: Average	OBJ: Grammar
17. ANS: B	DIF: Average	OBJ: Grammar

Essay

18. Students should recognize that Dickinson does not seem to fear death, but that she realizes it is impossible to predict what happens to a person after death. She also recognizes that death means parting with the people one is close to in life. Dickinson seems to believe in an immortal soul and to expect that immortality will accompany death. In "Because I could not stop for Death—," she speculates that after death, centuries may pass very quickly (presumably until Judgment Day). Some students may note that Dickinson seems to think that people are fundamentally alone and that the soul may in fact be more isolated in life than it is after death.

    Difficulty: *Average*

Objective: *Essay*

19. Students should recognize that the teachers in the poem often seem to teach their opposites; for example, thirst teaches water, the oceans teach the land, battles teach peace, and death teaches love. The lessons are more often positive (water, peace, love), while the teachers are more often negative and involve human suffering (thirst, battles, death). Dickinson's message thus might be that we appreciate joy only after suffering, or that we need both the good and the bad in life because negative experiences or the absence of something helps define its meaning. Some students may note that love and death and birds and snow are not precisely opposites, but that love may fear death and birds clearly fear, or at least want to avoid, the coming of snow. These students may suggest that Dickinson's message is that we learn the most from the things and experiences that we most fear.

    Difficulty: *Challenging*

    Objective: *Essay*

Walt Whitman's Poetry

Vocabulary Warm-up Exercises, p. 172

A. 1. astronomer
2. venturing
3. mechanics
4. moist
5. lectured
6. intermission
7. measureless
8. applause

B. Sample Answers
1. T; *Abeyance* is a temporary suspension.
2. F; A *filament* would be thin or slender.
3. T; *Gossamer* implies transparency.
4. T; *Isolated* people may be acutely conscious of solitude or loneliness.
5. T; *Melodious* means "tuneful."
6. F; A *promontory* would normally be located high up, on a crag or cliff.
7. F; An *unaccountable* explanation would not be logical, and it would probably not be credible.
8. T; All the rooms would be occupied.

Reading Warm-up A, p. 173

Sample Answers
1. he felt he would be nervous; People *venturing* to climb high mountains should be well prepared and in good physical condition.
2. (explaining the movements of the planets and stars); *astronomical*
3. a bunch of objects to be tinkered with; When they worked on my car engine, the *mechanics* found that the carburetor needed to be replaced.

4. (the breath of a few hundred people); The opposite of *moist* is *dry*.

5. (unable to voice an opinion, as the astronomer . . . the crowd); *addressed, delivered a talk*

6. <u>when they could leave the auditorium for a few minutes of fresh air</u>; *pause, break*

7. (they might clap a little); At the end of the concert, the violinist received thunderous *applause* from the audience.

8. <u>its mystery and . . . size</u>; *endless, boundless, infinite, unlimited*

Reading Warm-up B, p. 174

Sample Answers

1. <u>never really finished . . . held in . . . subject to periodic revision</u>; Since Thelma was not yet ready to start up her own business, she held her plans in *abeyance*.

2. (a long and winding thread); The writer uses the word *like* to compare the book to a long thread that parallels and records the poet's development.

3. <u>focusing only on one priority</u>; *solitary, lonely, alone*

4. <u>chaos, confusion, and misery</u>; *explicable, logical, comprehensible*

5. (. . . at the end of the medical middle ages . . . knowledge was . . . -thin); *figuratively*

6. <u>two thousand wounded men a day were pouring into Washington hospitals, and the beds in them were never vacant</u>; The opposite of *vacant* is *full* or *occupied*.

7. <u>Whitman found the inspiration to create . . . verse out of his hospital work in the poetry collection *Drum-Taps* . . .</u>; *tuneful*

8. (or rocky outcropping)

Literary Analysis: Free Verse, p. 175

Students' responses will vary. Some students may say that the free-verse version is a better reflection of the spider's spinning and the soul's freedom, that the short first line identifying the spider captures the idea of the spider alone on a promontory, and that the picked-up rhythm toward the final lines echoes the spider's tireless unreeling and speeding described in those lines. Other students may prefer a metrical version (if not the one provided), pointing out that while a spider may send out filament somewhat randomly to explore an area, the final web that it weaves is highly patterned.

Reading Strategy: Infer the Poet's Attitude, p. 176

1. B; 2. A; 3. A; 4. B; 5. C

Vocabulary Builder, p. 177

A. 1. B; 2. D; 3. A; 4. A

B. Possible Responses

1. I depart as air, I shake my white locks at the runaway sun, I spread my flesh out in eddies, and drift it in lacy jags.

2. Creeds and school in suspension, retiring back a while sufficed at what they are, but never forgotten.

C. 1. B; 2. C

Grammar and Style: Pronoun-Antecedent Agreement, p. 178

A. Students should circle each correct pronoun and underline its antecedent.

1. her; antecedent: Mrs. Pell
2. its; antecedent: volume
3. his; antecedent: Whitman
4. it; antecedent: company

B. 1. Whitman leans and loafs at his ease, observing a spear of summer grass.

2. Whitman notes that his ancestors include his parents and their parents.

3. When Whitman listened to the lecture, he became tired and sick from looking at the charts and diagrams and measuring them.

4. Whitman's noiseless, patient spider explores a large area, and it spins filaments out of its body, tirelessly unreeling them.

Enrichment: Science, p. 181

Suggested Responses

1. "When I Heard the Learn'd Astronomer":
How soon unaccountable *I became tired and sick,*
In the *mystical* moist night air
Look'd up *in perfect silence* at the stars.
"A Noiseless Patient Spider":
A noiseless *patient* spider
And you *O my soul*
in *measureless oceans* of space,
Ceaselessly musing, venturing, throwing, *seeking* the spheres to connect them
Till the gossamer thread you fling catch somewhere,
O my soul.

2. Yes. Like a scientist, Whitman emphasizes observation of the natural world.

3. Students may mention that a scientist would want to know the exact locations of stars, which are stars and which are planets, what kind of star each is, how the locations of stars as seen from Earth change with the seasons and time of the night, and so on.

4. Students may mention that a scientist would want to know what kind of spider this is, where it lives, what it eats, how long its lifespan is, and so on.

5. Students' poems may emphasize objective facts and measurements, and should avoid anthropomorphizing the stars or spider.

Selection Test A, p. 182

Critical Reading

1. ANS: C   DIF: Easy   OBJ: Literary Analysis

2. ANS: B	DIF: Easy	OBJ: Reading Strategy
3. ANS: C	DIF: Easy	OBJ: Literary Analysis
4. ANS: B	DIF: Easy	OBJ: Reading Strategy
5. ANS: C	DIF: Easy	OBJ: Comprehension
6. ANS: A	DIF: Easy	OBJ: Interpretation
7. ANS: D	DIF: Easy	OBJ: Reading Strategy
8. ANS: B	DIF: Easy	OBJ: Comprehension

Vocabulary and Grammar

9. ANS: B	DIF: Easy	OBJ: Vocabulary
10. ANS: C	DIF: Easy	OBJ: Grammar

Essay

11. Students may say that Americans still feel that immigrants make the nation stronger, by bringing new energy and ideas to the country. Accept responses that show examples of the contributions of diverse groups to the nation.

Difficulty: *Easy*

Objective: *Essay*

12. Students' essays should reflect that much of Whitman's poetry was positive about nature, work, life, democracy, and the variety of experiences that were available to people in nineteenth-century American. Students might use a variety of examples from the poetry as evidence.

Difficulty: *Easy*

Objective: *Essay*

Selection Test B, p. 185

Critical Reading

1. ANS: A	DIF: Average	OBJ: Comprehension
2. ANS: D	DIF: Challenging	OBJ: Reading Strategy
3. ANS: D	DIF: Easy	OBJ: Literary Analysis
4. ANS: D	DIF: Average	OBJ: Interpretation
5. ANS: B	DIF: Average	OBJ: Reading Strategy
6. ANS: C	DIF: Easy	OBJ: Interpretation
7. ANS: A	DIF: Average	OBJ: Reading Strategy
8. ANS: D	DIF: Challenging	OBJ: Comprehension
9. ANS: B	DIF: Average	OBJ: Interpretation
10. ANS: A	DIF: Easy	OBJ: Comprehension
11. ANS: C	DIF: Challenging	OBJ: Literary Analysis
12. ANS: A	DIF: Challenging	OBJ: Reading Strategy
13. ANS: D	DIF: Average	OBJ: Literary Analysis
14. ANS: D	DIF: Average	OBJ: Reading Strategy

Vocabulary and Grammar

15. ANS: B	DIF: Average	OBJ: Vocabulary
16. ANS: C	DIF: Average	OBJ: Grammar

Essay

17. Students should recognize that Whitman admired the average person, and was more likely to write about jobs that involved physical work, such as carpentry or mechanics, than about jobs that involve a lot of education, such as practicing law or medicine. They should also realize that America is bigger and includes more occupations than it did in Whitman's day. Students may wish to include some fairly recent occupations, such as computer programmer or astronaut.

Difficulty: *Easy*

Objective: *Essay*

18. Whitman seems to feel that death is not an unhappy event but rather one that he accepts as part of nature. By observing nature, Whitman learns about death. Some students may quote lines such as the following: "The smallest sprout shows there is really no death," and "to die is different from what anyone supposed, and luckier."

Difficulty: *Average*

Objective: *Essay*

19. Whitman's poetry shows that he values diversity of ethnic background, occupation, income level, and so on. It also shows that he admires the average person. Traveling through the United States, he found Americans from all walks of life to be admirable. Whitman also does not value formal advanced education, which especially in his day was accessible to only a few, any more than he values informal education, which people gain by observing life and nature.

Difficulty: *Challenging*

Objective: *Essay*

Writing About Literature—Unit 3

Compare and Contrast Literary Trends: Integrating Grammar Skills, p. 189

A. 1. repetitive

2. varied

3. repetitive

B. Students should provide answers with varied sentence beginnings, such as the following:

1. Unlike the Transcendentalists, Nathaniel Hawthorne and Herman Melville did not have an optimistic view of life.

2. Emily Dickinson, who was a hermit for much of her life, did not publish her poetry. She wrote in order to struggle privately with questions of life and death.

Writing Workshop—Unit 3

Reflective Essay: Integrating Grammar Skills, p. 191

Students should provide answers with varied sentence beginnings, such as the following:

1. I heard the wind howling. Then the door suddenly slammed, and the windows rattled.
2. Making choices is hard, but it is an important part of growing up.
3. My big sister is my best friend because she really listens to me. When I ask her for advice, she gives it, but usually she lets me make my own decisions.

Spelling—Unit 3

Proofreading Practice, p. 192

1. dimensions; 2. immature; 3. divisible; 4. possessors;
5. breathe; 6. visible; 7. muscles; 8. through;
9. commercial; 10. scientists; 11. ex-sailor;
12. especially; 13. dependent; 14. impossible;
15. interference; 16. explosions

Benchmark Test 4, p. 195

MULTIPLE CHOICE

1. ANS: B
2. ANS: D
3. ANS: D
4. ANS: A
5. ANS: C
6. ANS: B
7. ANS: B
8. ANS: C
9. ANS: A
10. ANS: B
11. ANS: A
12. ANS: A
13. ANS: C
14. ANS: D
15. ANS: B
16. ANS: B
17. ANS: A
18. ANS: A
19. ANS: D
20. ANS: C
21. ANS: B
22. ANS: B
23. ANS: B
24. ANS: D
25. ANS: D
26. ANS: A

ESSAY

27. Students' lists should use clear and vivid language to describe a real-life or fictional character.
28. Students' drafts should contain three important ideas, should include support for each idea, and should be well organized. The letter should be clearly organized. Because students are not being asked to revise their draft, there may be faulty transitions and some errors in spelling, punctuation, or grammar.
29. Students should clearly state a position, using the sentence stem *I think that there should be a law against _____*. Their supporting examples should clearly relate to the position statement and should each state a separate idea.